the meaning of

CARE FUL

How putting people before process
will deliver outstanding results
and transform our healthcare

Dr D J Brown, BMedSci BM BS

HCV Publishing

HCV PUBLISHING

Published by HCV Publishing
42 Moulsford House, Camden Road, London N7 0BE

First published by HCV Publishing 2009

1 3 5 7 9 10 8 6 4 2

Editor: Jo Swinnerton
Designer: Lou Millward

The moral right of the author has been asserted.

Printed in Great Britain by the MPG Books Group, Bodmin and King's Lynn

ISBN: 978-0-9563833-0-3

CONTENTS

To my father, who encouraged
me to become a doctor.

ACKNOWLEDGEMENTS

First and foremost, this book has been made possible by my friend
Jo Swinnerton, whose extraordinary skills as an editor made the
barely intelligible easily readable.

Many others have helped at various stages along the way.
John Wilson has encouraged me and supported me – despite my
tangents – throughout the effort to get HCV off the ground. Mona
Bitar, too, has supported this in so many ways. David Briggs, BJ
Cunningham, Meir Russ and Gary Spellins all had their hand in
developing the Three Circles and the theory behind the valuation
of human capital. Rupert Hucker taught me almost everything I
know about implementation – and gave permission for the use
of the Cliff-Face diagram. Sonja patiently helped us build the HCV
database. Simon Parlett created our website and Lou Millward
produced the book, against all odds.

Thanks also to my family – Jeremy, Jackie and my mother in
particular – for allowing me to use our personal stories, and, of
course, for supporting me unconditionally all these years.

More generally, this book would not have been possible without
the many teachers, colleagues and friends whose care, insight
and hard work taught me both the art and science of medicine.
Finally – without too much schmaltz, I hope – I'd like to thank
and acknowledge all those many patients whose trust and good
humour have taught me so much about courage and compassion.

INTRODUCTION

" 'Treat everyone as if they were your mother or father.' This, according to some, is the very definition of compassion." With these words I began an article in a national healthcare management magazine last year, exhorting readers to take seriously the need for better measurement of clinical leadership.

I began with that phrase because, as a practising doctor, I find it sad that not all healthcare is delivered with the compassion, humanity and care that patients deserve. Much that should happen naturally in such a caring profession seems to have been lost: unbalanced targets, thoughtless leadership, an emphasis on the short-term, inexpert political interference and seemingly endless reorganisation have all taken their toll. Healthcare has become less caring – both of its patients and its staff.

I mention staff, because in the dozen years during which I have worked both as a front-line doctor and an implementation consultant, helping hospitals and other organisations to implement change, I have seen that if patients are to be properly cared for, we need to have staff who feel fulfilled and motivated. And for that to happen, they need two things.

First, they have a need to be successful. Specifically, they must be able to demonstrate their success by delivering tangible results – both clinical and non-clinical – that they care about.

Second, they, like their patients, want to feel cared for and valued. They want their leaders and their peers to treat them with compassion, humanity and good humour.

These two things, in my experience, are not mutually exclusive. In fact, in healthcare they are mutually dependent. Despite how odd it sounds, to deliver the numbers, we must care for each other – and vice versa.

It is because of this belief – that we need both numerical rigour and compassionate care, and that they depend upon each other – that I have written this book. I hope that in some way it may inspire us as healthcare leaders to redouble our efforts to improve further the institutions in which we and our families are treated.

Because, as my first chapter demonstrates, it is we and our families who suffer, as much as anyone, from our failure to do so.

Dr D J Brown, BMedSci BM BS

CHAPTER 1

*Why healthcare should be
more like John Lewis*

I t was a hot, sunny week last summer when my mother started feeling unwell. Up until then she had been a healthy 76-year-old. She played badminton once a week, went for five-mile walks without a problem and enjoyed her keep-fit classes. She had never had a day's serious illness, had never been hospitalised and was on no medication.

Over the course of several days, she developed a flu-like illness: she had a persistently high temperature and a dry cough and lost her appetite. She didn't eat properly for about five days and, worse, she didn't drink enough either. She was in bed for several days, but didn't sleep well. While none of this was comfortable, it wasn't too serious.

After a week, though, she noticed a rash on her legs. She went to her GP. It seemed she was becoming systemically unwell, and he thought she should be seen at the hospital. She was admitted via A&E to the Medical Admissions Unit on a Thursday night. She was seen by the admitting physician the next day – within 12 hours as required by the Royal College of Physicians – and was assumed to be merely dehydrated. She had low sodium levels (about 118 instead of the more normal 135–145), so the doctors put her on IV fluids and the nurses encouraged her to drink.

Over the weekend, she was cared for by some lovely people. The nursing and ancilliary staff were friendly and compassionate. However, she was not seen by another senior doctor, and the only doctors available were for urgent cases. They were junior and very overworked.

It was at this point that things started to go wrong. As she was on a drip but also being encouraged to drink, her fluid intake went from 500ml to over 4 litres in a day – from under a pint to over a gallon. No one noticed until Saturday evening, when she started to become breathless and very, very anxious. Her temperature and flu-like symptoms had all disappeared and her rash was receding, but now her ECG – which was normal on admission – developed atrial fibrillation (AF). She felt as if her heart were trying to get out of her chest. By Sunday evening she had fallen into heart failure, frank pulmonary oedema, and was drowning in her own secretions. She was close to death and she knew it.

Fortunately, someone at last noticed the problem, at which point she was grossly fluid-restricted – starved of water – and put on a diuretic in order to reverse the problem. On Monday, for reasons that were not clear, her consultant changed – the person who had seen her on Friday was no longer her doctor. Unfortunately her new consultant did not see patients on a Monday because he had an endoscopy list. So this meant that she was not going to have a review by a senior doctor from Friday morning until Tuesday afternoon – four and a half days – the equivalent of being seen on Monday morning, then not again until Friday.

When she was eventually seen, the consultant ordered a battery of investigations to find out why she had gone into heart failure, including:

- CTPA (X-ray investigation of the pulmonary arteries)
- abdominal ultrasound scan
- several more chest X-rays
- exercise ECG stress test
- echocardiogram
- a battery of blood tests including cultures and various auto-antibody tests, thyroid function tests and so forth

By this time, her hands, face, arms and legs had swelled up. She was unable to walk properly. After several days she was moved to another long-term ward in order to continue her recovery.

She was seen by her consultant only once more – in order to discharge her several days later. She was sent home into the care of her daughter, who flew back from America, leaving her own children, to provide 24-hour care.

At this point, my previously capable mother was unable to look after herself. She developed occasional bouts of AF and was put on beta blockers in order to control this. They made her very tired. She couldn't walk far.

Slowly, over the coming months, she made progress back to normal. She made several outpatient visits to her consultant and to a cardiologist. Investigations continued as to why she developed AF. Three months later she was discharged from the hospital's care with a clean bill of health but without:

- a diagnosis – or any underlying reason for her heart failure, pulmonary oedema or AF
- any recognition that her condition may have been mismanaged
- any admission that the hospital may have made a near-fatal mistake
- any phone call or letter from the hospital to ask about her experience

My mother was unwilling to write a letter to the hospital explaining our concerns because one day she may go back to that hospital for another reason, and she doesn't want a reputation for being 'difficult'. The fact is, she was grossly fluid-overloaded during a period when her fluid status should have been closely monitored and carefully regulated. The NHS had probably spent £100,000 unnecessarily on her extra stay and her investigations.

The trouble is, no one knows that the hospital nearly killed my mother and no one has learned from it. That means that it could happen again. And maybe it has.

Thankfully, my mother is now fighting fit once again. She has resumed her keep-fit classes and can do her five-mile walks once again without a problem. She has not had another day's illness since this experience, and is once again on no regular medication.

But she's given up the badminton.

CARING FOR THE CUSTOMER

By way of a contrast, I'd like to tell you a story about a saucepan.

I was in John Lewis a few years ago, attempting to buy a saucepan. I was standing in the kitchen department – not a place in which I feel terribly confident – weighing a saucepan in each hand and wondering which would better suit my needs, when a man in brown overalls strolled past me, pushing a big trolley full of... well, full of kitchen stuff. He was clearly a warehouseman.

He saw me and stopped. Did I need some help? It was clear that I did. He offered a few opinions – hefting a few pans and comparing their merits. We discovered that the one I needed wasn't there. He went off to get some help and came back with one of his sales colleagues. Between the three of us we decided which pan I needed, and a few minutes later the overalls guy went back to pushing his trolley and continued on his way.

In which other shop would a warehouseman even notice that I was there, let alone recognise that I needed help? How many would know enough about their product to be able to help – or consider it their job to help?

Imagine if our healthcare organisations were run like John Lewis. Not only did this person, in a seemingly lowly position, have the confidence and capability to deal with my problem, but he also cared enough about my predicament to notice and do something about it. If we come back to my mother's story, I wonder who in the myriad of people looking after her in those first few days noticed that she should have had a fluid-balance chart. Did they notice and then not speak up? Or didn't they care? And how many of the senior doctors cared about the condition of the patients, or worried about how overworked the staff were on their wards at weekends?

When I tell my saucepan story to people, I find that they often have their own John Lewis stories. One person told me he took a faulty camera back to a different JL store without a receipt and was given not only a replacement camera, no questions asked, but also a partial cash refund because the price had dropped since buying it. Replacement camera plus £30. Based on your word as a customer. Nice.

The reason that this is possible is partly because John Lewis as an organisation is dedicated to – wait for it – the happiness of its staff. (Of course, this can't be to the exclusion of profitability or customer satisfaction – in fact John Lewis acknowledges that these things are interdependent.) I say that as if it were extraordinary – but what is extraordinary is not that a business should stress employee satisfaction as a driving force, but that taking such a stand is so rare. When you think about it, it seems obvious that all businesses – or organisations of any kind – should be run this way.

It is as a result of this stand that employees of John Lewis demonstrate something that most people – let alone those of us in healthcare – have never really known.

We call it 'performance ownership'.

PERFORMANCE OWNERSHIP

Performance ownership means having a real care for the reputation and success of the organisation that you work for – a real attachment to its purpose and how well it is doing. At John Lewis, people really do care that they are 'never knowingly undersold', and they really do care whether the customer has a good experience in their shop. The reputation of their organisation is actually important to them. They are proud of it – and they feel that they are genuinely part of it.

People tell me that this 'performance ownership' is possible only because John Lewis employees 'own' the shop (as partners). I reject this for two reasons: there are other examples where employees don't own the shop (I'll cover these in Chapter 11), and on a day-to-day basis it's not the certificates in their pockets that make them do it. It's what's in their heads – how they feel about their work. Share ownership may help, but it's not essential.

My work with healthcare clients over the last few years has been directed towards making performance ownership a reality in healthcare. I believe not only that it's possible, but also that it's essential we do this if the NHS is to thrive. Performance ownership is better for the patient – and it's necessary also for the efficiency improvements and cost savings that we are going to need in the future.

Performance ownership is better for the patient because in hospitals it means noticing not that someone is dithering over a saucepan but that they are in pain, or becoming fluid-overloaded like my mother, or maybe just lost. Patients are not just treated; they are cared for.

Performance ownership is better for efficiencies and costs because it makes people want to improve their organisation. They put in the discretionary effort needed to make things more efficient – and greater efficiency can lead to better clinical outcomes as well as reductions in costs.

And finally, it is better for staff because working in such an organisation gives them a real sense of satisfaction and happiness in their work.

So far, so obvious, you might think. But the question is, how do we develop performance ownership in our healthcare organisations?

TRANSFORMING HEALTHCARE

To some extent, my mother's story provided the impetus for me to write this book. But the idea for the book began much earlier, when I left the NHS myself 10 years ago. I wasn't always a doctor: I once worked in city institutions, then re-found my childhood vocation to become a doctor. I trained for five years, but once in the job, I quickly lost my faith in medicine. I found myself working for organisations that seemed hell-bent on breaking me. I remember the surge of anger I once felt when I was asked by one of my well-meaning patients: 'Don't you ever go home?' I was sleep-deprived and gently bullied for several years until I gave up. My colleagues and friends must have been made of sterner stuff. Or maybe they just didn't think they had a choice. Either way, I was pleased to leave behind organisations that I felt were profoundly in need of change.

I left medicine when I was given the opportunity to work as an implementation consultant whose job it was to help change organisations. That seemed pretty appropriate, considering. I soon learned how hard it was to really change such things – to help people modify en masse the way that they work. People, it seems, have a strange way of resisting change, even when it is in their best interests. (I'll talk more about that in Chapter 4.)

Over the years I became interested in how cultural change comes about, particularly within the healthcare industry. I set up a company called Human Capital Valuation, which aims to transform hospitals, making them better places to work and better places to be treated as a patient. As the company's name suggests, it focuses primarily on helping organisations to gain maximum value from the people who work for them.

The problems that prevent such excellence tend to be the same whether you work for a bank, an oil company or a hospital – an unbalanced focus on profit and too little emphasis on what makes staff feel successful, motivated and committed. Yet we all know that people are the key to everything – to your success as well as your failure.

Drawn back by that childhood vocation, I returned to medicine in 2004 and now work in A&E, as well as running my company. The NHS changed while I was away. Junior doctors seem less overworked and better cared for, although it often seems to be at the expense of their seniors. There is much more computing power in evidence. Investigations have improved and treatment has continued to accelerate. Yet there is much still to improve, as my mother's example showed.

But what I did realise, and still know, is that healthcare is teeming with talented staff – extraordinary individuals of the very highest calibre. Most industries would give away half their assets to get their hands on staff of the quality – highly trained, intelligent and self-motivated – that is enjoyed by healthcare organisations. So if that is the case, why aren't our healthcare organisations more successful?

It's true that there are some great examples of fantastic places to work – world-leading organisations filled with happy and motivated staff. Yet the sad thing is that this is unusual. For the most part, this extraordinary human capital asset is needlessly squandered: high-quality individuals and teams are often demotivated and unhappy, with equally unhappy consequences for patients and for the efficiency and reputation of the places in which they are treated.

Yet – as this book sets out to prove – it needn't be so.

CHAPTER 2

Why we should value our human capital

Ionce worked with an independent hospital where the Financial Director took a particularly extreme view of what was important to success: 'It's volume that counts,' he insisted. 'Getting the patients through the door. Everything else is just soft stuff. If someone's no good we should simply get rid of them and hire someone better.' Given that I was trying to persuade him to develop and nurture the 'soft stuff', I had a serious challenge on my hands. It's true that that we can overindulge in too much 'soft stuff' at the expense of good management systems, but I strongly disagreed with him. He – and his 'hard-nosed' colleagues – can so easily squander the talented and motivated staff that deliver healthcare to our friends and families. By demotivating them he risks making them, and his hospital, unsafe. His approach verges on the negligent.

To counter this, over the last few years I have developed a way to explain more eloquently why I think this is the case and why, to develop real excellence, you must focus *jointly* on operations, patients and people.

I called my company Human Capital Valuation because we believe you can put a value on human capital just as easily as on financial capital, and that by doing so, you can drive both growth and improvement. An organisation is not simply a machine into which you put investment in order to get results. It is more complex than that. Each organisation is a finely tuned balance of capital and talent.

In the past, an organisation was measured solely by the value of its tangible assets – work in progress, assets, capital employed and retained profit. So businesses tended to focus entirely on increasing value by building capacity, developing new products, improving efficiency and increasing margins and so on. What that didn't take into account was the qualities of the people who worked for that company: their motivation, their capability and their willingness to stay in their jobs. Let me explain how this works by referring to the diagram opposite.

CIRCLE 1 (left, 'Financial Capital'): We take money from investors (taxpayers or shareholders) and put it into a budget with which we build capacity to deliver healthcare. This creates demand from patients. The volume of patients largely determines the size of the financial surplus. These are the traditional 'book values' on the balance sheet.

THE THREE CIRCLES

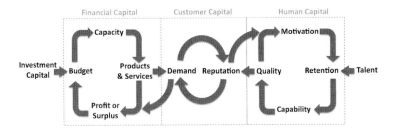

CIRCLE 2 (centre, 'Customer Capital'): The demand from patients is also affected by the reputation of the organisation and vice versa. The better the hospital, the more a patient will want to go there. In commerce, demand and reputation are the 'goodwill', the intangibles, which predict the future value of a company.

CIRCLE 3 (right, 'Human Capital'): The reputation of your hospital is, however, principally dictated by the quality of the care it delivers. This quality is largely determined by the capability of your staff, which is influenced by levels of staff retention, the talent that can be attracted and staff motivation. Critically, motivation is itself largely determined by quality and reputation: everyone wants to do a good job, working in a great hospital.

These qualities of human capital are not traditionally used to value companies and yet, in a service environment, and especially in healthcare, it is these qualities that determine the long-term success of an organisation.

For simplicity, I have abbreviated this complex model into something more manageable (see overleaf). It is easy to see that these circles feed off each other. Motivated, capable staff deliver a high-quality service which creates a good reputation, which not only causes patients to demand more services, but also has a positive impact on motivation. This demand then generates cash that can be used to build more capacity and deliver more services. It is also easy to see that demotivated and poorly trained employees can destroy your reputation, causing a fall-off in demand and a fall in volume.

It is common for organisations to neglect or merely pay lip-service to the human capital circle and concentrate instead on measuring financial capital.

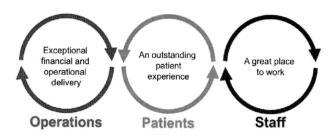

As we shall see, measuring customer/patient capital as well as human capital is not difficult, and it helps us to improve financial and operational results.

The ideas and the programme that I outline in this book are based on the need to balance these three circles and at the same time to ensure that all staff have the right mix of challenge and support (see page 28). Without this, they won't provide the efficient and effective levels of care that are being demanded by patients and investors.

Valuing your human capital is the key to transforming your organisation.

CHAPTER 3

*The CAREFUL Programme:
seven steps to creating
performance ownership*

patients and works to improve their experience. It responds also to staff and their needs, to enable them to be more efficient.

ENERGETIC: Leaders work constantly to improve the way in which they lead the organisation. They use their skills to positively influence and energise the people who work for them. The organisation recognises leadership development as being as important as clinical development.

FOCUSED: Everyone in the organisation sees beyond what is happening today and strives for goals that may seem impossible. The organisation does not tolerate unacceptable behaviour or attitudes that work against this effort.

UNIFORM: The organisation is an efficient machine where repetitive tasks are done right first time, every time, freeing up time for staff to provide 'service on top'. It properly documents, controls and improves its processes.

LEADING: A leading hospital knows where it stands – it knows its first or best position. And being good at one thing makes everyone in that hospital want to do more of it, to sustain that reputation. As a result, they do everything else well, too. They are proud of and work hard for their hospital – they have found performance ownership.

You will find the description of each stage and each quality in Chapters 5–11. In each chapter I explain why this quality is necessary and what it means for your organisation. I explain how to achieve this quality in your organisation, starting with the bare essentials – the things that you *must* do – then I add further ideas for ways in which you can turn Hospital B into Hospital A.

Before I do, though, I'm going to offer you a small challenge. I would not be surprised if, at this point, you are thinking one of several things:

'We already do that.'

'That's not possible.'

Or maybe just: 'I can think of several reasons why he's probably wrong.'

I know this, because I have heard all of these many times before. It's just sheer resistance. It's common, it's obstructive – and it's time we dealt with it.

CHAPTER 4

*Change management and
the problem of implementation*

I once worked for a client that needed to redesign its supply chain in order to save millions of pounds in wasted costs. The company needed to renegotiate contracts with all its main suppliers and work out better ways for goods and people to be delivered to its many sites. This was a hugely complex programme of change that required immense technical skills as well as the ability to influence a wide range of people.

The person responsible for this programme had recently been appointed to the role of 'procurement manager', a title that didn't do justice to the immensity of the challenge that he faced. His team was very junior and had no experience of managing change on this scale. His boss hired us, a small team of experienced consultants, to help him to create and execute a plan to save all this wasted money.

Over the course of several weeks, it became clear that the procurement manager was doing everything underhand that he could in order to get rid of us. His aim was to undermine our credibility and to get us out of his department. He avoided all contact with us and spent time trying to make out that his department's work – which was of terrible quality – belonged to us. He spent time bad-mouthing us to his colleagues, who were working with us on other projects and had made up their own minds. His tactics became more obvious as the weeks went by. Eventually, the tension rose to such a point that his boss took the only step available.

He sacked his new procurement manager.

What was going on here? Instead of welcoming us as a way to improve his team's capability and reduce his own workload, this man acted consistently against his own interests and paid the price by losing his job. Such behaviour is hard to understand – especially if you are new to change implementation.

The answer is fairly simple. We're all human and hold strongly to our ideas of what sort of person we are, how good a job we do, and what is important to us. If someone comes along and says 'This all needs to change' or even simply 'It looks like you could do with some help', it can be uncomfortable and a threat to our security, our identity and our pride. People do not actually resist change per se – on the contrary, most people welcome change. What they resist is *being* changed. It is the emotions evoked by being changed that will cause problems when you set out to transform your organisation.

As I said at the end of Chapter 3, suggestions of change often meet with resistance. Here are six reasons why your staff – or you – might resist the changes needed to transform your organisation.

1. Threat to security
A fear of losing what you have. This can be your job, position, sense of direction, territory or work relationships. Any threat to move people around and change these things, particularly job descriptions, is so unsettling that it easily overrides reason.

2. Threat to identity
A need to maintain what you are (rather than what you have). This can be a real or perceived threat to self-esteem, competence or established position. Our procurement manager clearly felt this acutely.

3. Conflict of values
The 'over my dead body' issue. Change may appear to undermine the current value system or culture of the individual or of the organisation by implying that they're not good enough, even if this is not necessarily the case. A good example of this would be clinicians faced with cost savings, if they felt that the savings would be dangerous or that they might threaten their judgement and professionalism.

4. Inherent problems with change
The 'Whoa! Slow down' problem. Stability is more important to some people than others – and a lot of people think that going in a new direction will be too difficult or too terrible. Many have difficulty embracing the magnitude or speed of change, or the fact that it is irreversible.

5. Lack of belief
The 'here we go again' syndrome. If a person has been subjected to lots of previously unsuccessful changes in their organisation, they will, naturally, be suspicious of yet another set of initiatives. They will lack faith in any new changes and will be unable to see the likely benefits.

6. False optimism

'Oh, we're doing all that.' This was the response of an HR director of a hospital I talked to recently about some of the concepts in this book. I had worked in his hospital and I knew they weren't doing 'all that'. The place was deeply dysfunctional. Of course, no one can get away with this if they are measuring their results, something I insist upon frequently throughout this book. In fact, this last objection is the hardest to overcome, because you do have to install measurement systems, which is hard, just to face up to reality.

I suggested in Chapter 3 that you may feel some of these 'resistances' yourself. That's normal. But how can you and your staff overcome them? There's no single answer, but there are some things that I have learned about how to make change easier which may help you as you work through the CAREFUL Programme.

1. Be positive and visible

Repeat the benefits. Be encouraging and compassionate. Smile (genuinely). Never berate or blame someone for a problem – it will come back to bite you. Never announce an initiative then retreat to your office and wait for someone else to deliver it. It's your challenge too.

2. Let the people do it for themselves

Find ways for staff to make their own changes. Set up Action Teams (see Chapter 6) rather than ruling by decree, so that staff create and implement their own changes rather than being changed from 'above'. Then congratulate, reward and recognise their contributions.

3. Recognise and understand resistance

Don't get cross or frustrated when staff resist. Get closer. Find out what's bugging people and deal with their concerns. Negotiate. Give them time to understand. Involve them.

4. Only believe the numbers

Time and again throughout this book, I emphasise the need for installing systems to measure and manage what you are trying to implement. A verbal report is quick and easy, but often worthless. A doctor won't accept that a heart rate is 'reasonable': they demand the number. Equally, a target isn't meaningful unless it has a number attached. (Saying that 'staff absenteeism is down to 3%' is vastly more meaningful than 'staff absenteeism is down' or 'is acceptable'.) Remember the adage 'In God we trust, all else bring data'. Have command of the evidence.

5. Work hard on alignment

Resistant members of staff will set other members of your team against each other. Don't let them. Make sure that everyone in the senior team is completely aligned with the overall vision and targets. Help them learn how to articulate these aims.

6. Do one thing well

Don't bite off too many things at once. If you can address one problem at a time, it helps you to concentrate and move faster. Succeed at one thing, then move on.

7. Persist

A friend of mine has a saying: 'Persistence pays the bills.' He's right. You will have to become an expert at persistence. Persistence at different stages needs different skills (see 'The cliff face of implementation', page 32).

While you are thinking about persistence, it is important also to understand how to balance challenge and support as you encourage your staff to change the way they work. Challenge alone or support alone are not enough – you need both, and in the right quantities (see opposite), if staff are to be motivated and successful.

To support the seven principles above, I want to suggest that you develop three simple skills – leadership rounds, talking up and thank-you notes – which I have described on pages 29–32. Do these before you do anything else in this book, as a foundation for what is to follow.

CHALLENGE AND SUPPORT

To persuade anyone to change the way they work requires a fine balance of *challenge* and *support*. Challenge – which must be willingly accepted by the individual rather than imposed on them – can be anything that requires extra effort or capability. Support consists of those things that help to develop or nurture the necessary capabilities. Creating the right mixture of these two things is the key to success.

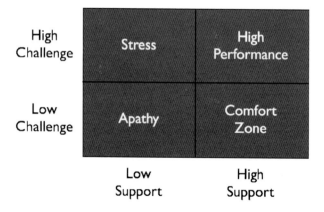

	Low Support	High Support
High Challenge	Stress	High Performance
Low Challenge	Apathy	Comfort Zone

Apathy: With too little of either challenge or support, jobs are meaningless. People find excitement and motivation elsewhere in their lives. A good example might be a night watchman: nothing much happens and no one much cares.

Comfort zone: Too much support without any real challenge may seem pleasant for a while but soon becomes cloying and seems a waste of time. It also rarely produces excellence. Many 'support' departments – almost by definition – suffer from this.

Stress: Too much challenge without enough support may cause short-term exhilaration, but soon causes burnout, even fear and isolation. *The Apprentice*, anyone?

High performance: With the right mixture of challenge and support, people grow: their capabilities and their motivation both improve and they derive real satisfaction from their jobs. Because they are helped to deliver, they deliver.

It's important to realise that the nature of 'support' required by high-performance staff – much of which we discuss in this book – is totally different from that enjoyed by those in the 'comfort zone': it means more hands-on training and individual coaching and fewer 'team-building' exercises and away-days (which may be fun but do nothing to respond to individual needs). Don't be surprised if moving your 'comfort zone' staff into the high-performance box causes stress. It will. But it will be worth it.

THREE SIMPLE SKILLS
Visibility of leaders is vitally important to staff. As I said earlier, it is no good delivering an initiative and then disappearing while someone else implements it. You, as the leader, need to be right there, helping, encouraging and rewarding results. Leadership rounds, talking up and thank-you notes are three small but significant ways to impress upon people the seriousness and strength of your own commitment as their leader.

LEADERSHIP ROUNDS
It is essential for senior leaders to be visible and approachable on a regular basis if staff are to feel engaged with their organisation. After all, how can leaders know what is really going on unless they spend time visiting and talking to their staff? It would be rather like a doctor treating a patient by email without ever meeting them.

Leadership rounds must focus on the positive and on the individual, otherwise staff will think you are there to catch them out. I recommend that you ask three questions:

1. What's going well?
2. Who's doing a great job?
3. What tools or equipment do you need to do your job?

Then take it from there. You must impose a proper structure on this part of your work; write down what your staff tell you, file and monitor the information and follow it up.

Avoid the temptation to fix problems during the rounds – that's not what they're for. Their chief purpose is for you to listen to and talk to your staff. If a problem comes up, note it down and deal with it later, otherwise it will feel like an inspection.

Making time for leadership rounds can seem difficult, but it pays dividends. You will better understand and respond to the day-to-day needs of staff; you will be viewed more positively; and, properly executed, leadership rounds will reduce ad hoc requests because staff can rely on having face-to-face time with you in the future.

Such leadership behaviours are difficult to introduce into an organisation – for some people they require a change in entrenched habits. But leaders do need to change their frame of reference and start thinking more readily about the work environment from the point of view of their staff.

FOLLOW THE LEADER

A CEO in one hospital I once worked in had a reputation for being aloof and constantly in his office dealing with email. A recent staff survey had been scathing of his style, so he adopted daily leadership rounds, choosing a different area of the hospital each day.

He soon discovered a lot about the day-to-day work of the hospital that had been hidden from him – and staff found that he was much more approachable and capable than they thought. Because he kept a log book, he was able to hold his leadership team to account for following up on the things he had discussed with clinical staff. He reckoned that by being proactive his rounds saved him several hours a week.

THANK-YOU NOTES

I recommend that leaders write regular letters of thanks to individual staff to acknowledge their work and the effect that it has on the organisation. Leadership rounds will provide all the material you need to decide who should be thanked and for what. Don't get your PA to write them and sign them on your behalf. And don't use email. The best thank-you notes take the form of a simple, hand-written greetings card, explaining what the person contributed, who passed on the information, and how their contribution improved the experience of patients and staff.

Experience tells us that maintaining enthusiasm for thank-you letters can be difficult. As with all implementation, it requires commitment from senior leaders and persistence. This means measuring and monitoring what letters are written by which leaders to whom – and making sure every leader is doing their bit. But if you are in doubt about their worth, I can tell you that I have seen staff laminate their thank-you notes and place them next to their work area, so proud were they to have their efforts praised.

Example of a thank-you note

> *Dear Kate,*
> *Tony tells me that while you and your team were on duty this weekend, you helped him reorganise the stock rooms as required by our last inspection. He tells me that this means we now won't lose any theatre time this week, as we feared. I really appreciate the extra effort and help that you put in because we know that cancelling theatre time can be very traumatic for patients and their families. Thank you.*

TALKING UP

Another tool you can use is 'talking up'. This combats the pernicious 'us and them' syndrome that builds up in large organisations. It's easy for one department to blame another when things go wrong, but it's damaging to staff morale and discourages collaboration between departments.

Talking up means describing your hospital, your colleagues and your peers in a positive way – that is, telling other staff and patients how good they are or how well qualified or successful. For example, it's reassuring to patients and staff to hear that your hospital has the newest equipment or the highest success rate in a particular area. Talking up sets a good example, becomes part of the culture and reinforces the positivity we need.

THE CLIFF-FACE OF IMPLEMENTATION – THE STAGES OF PERSISTENCE

It is worth expanding on the idea of persistence. I have a lot of experience of implementing change, and there is no doubt that it can be difficult – both for those leading and for those coping with the changes. Some of the ideas described in this chapter are easy. The ideas in later chapters become more and more difficult. The common thread is that each new change requires persistence.

To help, here's an analogy: you decide one day to climb a mountain and ski down the other side. You have to persuade your friends to come with you – all the way. You will need to go through several stages of persistence:

1. Getting started: you need to clearly articulate the end point – how great it will be to reach the top. I call this VISIONING.

2. Back-sliding: when things get tough, early on your friends will try to give up, finding good reasons to go home and watch TV. You need the skills of PROMOTION to keep them with you.

3. The long haul: the tedious, dangerous, exhausting climb will involve making mistakes and – mainly – trying not to fall off. Your job is to support your friends. This is COACHING.

4. The view from the top: when you make it to the top, you should rest a while and take in the view – and you should phone home and tell people how good it is. We call this IMAGING.

5. On the other side: you need to continue the good work, having got to the top. You need to DEMONSTRATE the benefits so your friends will come with you again.

The Implementation Cliff Face

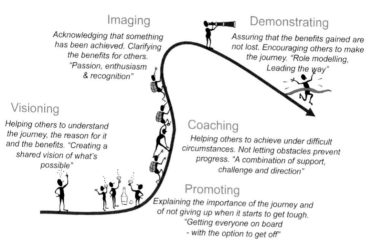

Imaging
Acknowledging that something has been achieved. Clarifying the benefits for others. "Passion, enthusiasm & recognition"

Demonstrating
Assuring that the benefits gained are not lost. Encouraging others to make the journey. "Role modelling, Leading the way"

Visioning
Helping others to understand the journey, the reason for it and the benefits. "Creating a shared vision of what's possible"

Coaching
Helping others to achieve under difficult circumstances. Not letting obstacles prevent progress. "A combination of support, challenge and direction"

Promoting
Explaining the importance of the journey and of not giving up when it starts to get tough. "Getting everyone on board - with the option to get off"

HOW PEOPLE LEARN AND THE IMPORTANCE OF NUMBERS

I'd like to finish this chapter with an important point about adult learning. I mentioned in the introduction how success – the opposite of resistance – can only really be demonstrated through numbers. I continually emphasise in this book the importance of numbers and systems as a way to help people measure, and therefore demonstrate, their success.

So, the groundwork has been done. Leadership rounds, thank-you letters and talking up have all started – and so we have begun the journey from Hospital B to Hospital A. Now for the seven stages.

CHAPTER 5

Committed

'Be clear'

A friend of mine recently had minor surgery on her hand. She had skewered herself trying to remove an avocado stone. Thankfully no lasting damage was done, so she makes light of it. She makes her friends squirm by describing the accident in gory detail, but she's never considered telling her employer about her mishap. Who would? However, if she'd worked for the international company DuPont, she'd have been sacked for not doing so.

Sound extreme? Before you pass judgement, there's one thing you should know about DuPont: they are the undisputed world leaders in industrial safety. The safety record of DuPont puts every other organisation in the world to shame.

The story of this goes back to the inter-war years. At that point, the company was already forward-thinking in industrial safety. However, it made munitions in the First World War and during that time a lot of people were killed in its factories. The graph showing the number of fatalities in its manufacturing sites shows an enormous blip between 1914 and 1918. Because of that, DuPont committed itself to eliminating fatalities and serious injuries entirely.

One of the most notable things it did was to place the house of every factory manager inside the factory. By putting the manager's home, family and possessions into the same position of risk as that of his employees, DuPont ensured that the manager had a vested interest in preventing the place from exploding. By the time the Second World War came along, the same graph showed not a murmur: major incidents continued to fall throughout.

By the end of the 20th century, the company could no longer use 'fatalities and serious injuries' as a measure. Any disturbance from zero was too rare to be useful. It started measuring other things, which predicted the likelihood of an accident – including accidents at home. As a DuPont employee you are contractually obliged to report accidents at home. The company has worked out that accidents are not random. They happen to unsafe people, and if you're unsafe at home you're probably going to be unsafe at work – hence the need to report avocado-related stabbings. And if you do something demonstrably unsafe at work (like standing on your desk), you're not welcome – just in case the next shortcut you take causes an explosion.

The key elements of the DuPont philosophy are:

- Managers at every level are responsible for preventing injuries and illnesses.
- Safety must be a part of every employee's training.
- People are the most important element of a health and safety programme.

There is much more to the DuPont philosophy and practice, and I do it an injustice by summarising it so briefly. For a complete description, see *Industrial Safety Is Good Business: The DuPont Story* by William J Mottell (John Wiley & Sons, 1995). It is a masterclass in commitment.

Therein lies the reason I use DuPont as an example in this chapter. It exemplifies what commitment means in an organisation:

- Be clear about your 'first or best' position. What makes you worth working for or doing business with? Are you the safest, the cheapest, the fastest; do you have the best technology or the best customer service?
- Set clear numerical targets at every level.
- Make sure that your leaders behave in a way that supports the first or best position.

DuPont's first or best position was simply to be the safest company in the world. Its target was zero accidents. And its behaviour backed that up – the safety rules were clear, strict and enforced absolutely at every level, from trainee to CEO.

The last point – demonstrable behaviour – is important. Commitment is not just a decision. It's also a process. Once you have stated your aim, you must back it up with appropriate behaviour.

Take, as a simple example, a man who wants to pass his driving test. He books a test date, which is the aim. But he backs that up with supporting behaviour – he takes driving lessons, he learns the Highway Code, he practises driving with friends and family, he checks with his instructor how well he's doing and works on his weak points. It is this behaviour that shows he is committed to passing. Merely saying 'I want to learn to drive' is not in itself proof of commitment, in the same way that a vision statement – 'We want to be the best!' – is meaningless without measurable targets and behaviour to back it up.

WHAT IS A COMMITTED ORGANISATION?

A **committed** organisation has a clear FIRST OR BEST POSITION.

A **committed** organisation underlines this with DEMONSTRABLE BEHAVIOUR.

A **committed** organisation has targets that are BALANCED across the Three Circles (see page 17).

A **committed** organisation has targets at EVERY LEVEL of leadership.

THE IMPORTANCE OF BALANCE – THE FOUR-HOUR WAIT

For a target to be meaningful, it must be pursued with some thought for balance within your organisation. This cautionary tale will demonstrate how things can go awry.

In 2003, amid growing public concern about long waits in A&E, the Blair administration introduced draconian penalties for any hospital that failed to see, treat or dispatch within four hours every patient that entered A&E. ('Dispatched' could mean sent home or admitted to the hospital.)

The government exerted pressure on hospitals to meet the target by simple but drastic means; each breach of the target could lead to severe penalties of several thousand pounds of reduced spending in the hospital. This filtered through the CEO/board members, divisional directors and department managers to the nurses and doctors on the shop floor.

I experienced the effects of this first-hand when I returned to work in A&E after taking a few years out of medicine, just as the targets began to bite. I came back from seeing my first patient and was approached by the 'Throughput Nurse' – or, to put it more simply, 'Nurse in Charge of Making Sure That No One Stayed More Than Four Hours in the Department'.

'What are you doing with this patient?' she asked.

'I'm going to wait until I get his blood tests back to decide whether he needs to be admitted or not.'

Without hesitation, she replied: 'Oh, no you're not, Doctor. You're going to make up your mind right now. If we need to admit him, we must make that decision right now. If he goes home, then he goes home now.'

I was taken aback. I insisted that I couldn't judge the clinical need until I knew what his results were. 'That's irrelevant. If there's any chance we might admit him, then he needs to come in.' And so we admitted him.

I quickly learned that for every breach, someone got a kicking – and that very soon translated into a change in behaviour. If you didn't want to be humiliated or quite literally shouted at, you got the patient out of the department – whether they'd been treated or not. You handed them over, sometimes mid-treatment – never a great idea when everyone's busy, tired and prone to errors – and hoped that nothing would go wrong. It worked, to a point. Patients generally were 'dispatched' within four hours. But they weren't necessarily treated in that time, and often they were admitted unnecessarily, only to be sent home hours later.

Let's examine this in the light of the Three Circles in Chapter 2. This is a well-managed target executed brilliantly, but it's completely unbalanced. On the whole, it doesn't take into account clinical need. It creates demand from patients (because they know they'll seen the same day, so they come to A&E instead of going to their GP) and yet creates no satisfaction in the staff.

TARGETS WORK – IF THEY'RE BALANCED

After reading this, you may be surprised to discover that I am an ardent supporter of targets. It's true that they can have unintended consequences. The unbalanced nature of the four-hour wait can have a negative impact on patients and staff, as we have seen. Nonetheless, it has caused a sea-change in the way in which patients are seen in A&E. Most consultants in this area agree that targets have done more good than harm by helping people to focus on the way in which demand is managed. We should be rightly proud of the efficiencies of our A&E departments. Targets are good in principle, providing they are balanced. We actually need more targets, not fewer.

The problem is that many of the targets demanded of senior leaders in healthcare these days are handed down either by the Department of Health or by shareholders. They tend to change with the political and financial climate. Most targets concentrate on finance and operations because investors (DoH or shareholders) are primarily interested in Circle 1, finance and operations. Leaders do need to meet these targets, of course, but it is vital that they keep the wider needs and aims of their organisation in mind, and not allow every new target to unbalance those things.

In summary, **balance**, across the Three Circles, is vital if you are to sustain your commitment and have targets that are meaningful. In the above example, operations benefited – but patients and staff did not.

WHAT'S THE BENEFIT OF COMMITMENT?

Commitment helps to align everyone from top to bottom. Everyone knows the key targets and priorities, what their organisation stands for and how to behave. At DuPont, no one is in any doubt about whether to stand on their desk to change a light bulb. Safety always comes first.

But commitment has a wider importance. Setting out the intent of the organisation helps people to solve problems in context. This is where a clear 'first or best' position helps. There is one airline, for instance, that is 'best' at being the lowest-cost airline. Staff are, allegedly, banned from charging their mobile phones at work because it wastes electricity. This may not be true – but such stories help staff to decide how to behave in other situations.

Commitment motivates staff. Commitment makes it clear why their organisation is worth working for. If staff are motivated, the rate of staff turnover and absenteeism goes down, which in turn improves clinical quality and patient care.

WHAT HAPPENS IF AN ORGANISATION LACKS COMMITMENT?

Working in an organisation that lacks commitment can be a demoralising affair. Here are a few examples of the many ways in which commitment can be lacking. Having talked to many people about this over the years, I would guess that everyone has experienced some of this, in one form or another. The boxes on pages 41 and 42 provide concrete examples.

- It's not clear if an organisation does anything particularly well – and there are plenty of things it does badly.
- Leaders talk about 'excellence' or 'people being our greatest asset', but then act in a way that undermines these assertions.
- The organisation becomes obsessed with a single target, to the detriment of the many other things that are important.
- Everyone works really hard, but no one has any clear idea what they contribute to the overall success of the organisation.

WORDS WITHOUT NUMBERS

I work occasionally in a hospital that has a super-glossy magazine that is sent to all employees once a month. In one issue was this little gem: 'Patients and the quality of their care throughout the hospital underpin the Trust's recently approved top ten objectives for 2009/10.'

If you're a patient, I'm sure you'll find that a big relief. Or maybe you are alarmed that in prior years, they had something else to worry about? Wait, though – there's more. Here are the top ten objectives in all their glory (number 7 is my personal favourite).

1. Deliver excellent clinical outcomes
2. Improve patient safety
3. Deliver high quality patient experience (sic)
4. Deliver waiting time targets
5. Achieve sustainable financial health
6. Develop and enable staff
7. Progress strategic development
8. Work with partners to improve patient pathways
9. Develop world-class research and development and excellent education
10. Develop governance and risk management

I asked one of the nursing staff what she thought of the magazine. She looked at it as if for the first time. 'Oh, that – I don't really read it,' she said. In truth, I had never seen any member of staff pick it up or read it.

The point is that these are all statements of the staggeringly obvious. Every hospital is, or should be, striving to meet these same objectives. What staff need to know is: how are they going to deliver the result and how are they going to measure their progress towards these targets?

WORDS WITHOUT MEANING

A friend who worked in a publishing company once returned to work one Monday morning to find that the office had been decorated – without prior consultation – with words indicating how committed the organisation was to the important aspects of the business: 'Creative', 'Inspiring', 'Imaginative' were stencilled across the walls. The reaction from the staff was, she said, minimal. The words may have impressed visiting clients (although probably not), but it certainly didn't change the way anyone worked.

The net effect of this is that staff are either lost, demotivated or – at worst – working in the wrong direction, against everyone else, often believing that they're doing the right thing. In short, confusion reigns.

WHY DON'T WE HAVE COMMITMENT IN OUR HEALTHCARE ORGANISATIONS?

There are a number of barriers to creating commitment in an organisation. These are some of the most common.

COMPLACENCY

I've heard a lot of objections throughout my management career, mainly from the board, about the ideas suggested in this chapter, including such things as: 'We don't need to tell the shop floor employees all this stuff,' or 'Oh, we've got that covered – we already have those targets.' They either don't want to change, or don't see the need to do so.

LACK OF SENIOR LEADERSHIP ALIGNMENT

The senior teams in most well-run organisations try to find at least one day a quarter to go away and review and plan the overall direction of the organisation. They certainly do it once a year – and there is good reason for doing this. You need different types of meeting for different types of discussion.

I recently asked a hospital exec team, 'How often do you take time away to discuss the overall performance of the organisation?' 'Oh, we don't bother with that. We just have a weekly meeting,' said the CEO. In this weekly meeting, which I have attended, they talk mainly about the day-to-day running of the organisation and the pressing issues of the moment. It had just never occurred to this team that a separate meeting to discuss the bigger issues – how to create alignment and clarity in their organisation – would be beneficial. Many senior leaders, and upcoming clinical leaders in particular, lack experience of, and the skills for, facilitating conversations about high-level targets and their overall vision for the organisation. They have never been trained to do so, and often they've never seen *their* seniors do so either.

PERSONAL AGENDAS

In some instances, personal agendas may dominate. Some years ago, the company that I worked for was hired to help with cost reduction for a water company in south London. At the end of a year, the project had not been a success – the operations department hadn't budged an inch – even though the head of operations had been overtly supportive. The team discovered only as the project ended that he had spent the entire year blocking the efforts of his own colleagues to save money because he fundamentally disagreed with the CEO's aims. This lack of alignment at the top caused the entire project to fail.

INADEQUATE MEASUREMENT SYSTEMS

Measurement systems exist for most operational or financial targets. But for many patient-centred and staff-centred measures, organisations are often sorely lacking in such systems. Those that do exist can be confusing or conflicting. Many organisations have a long way to go in order to put rigorous systems in place.

Much of this, historically, stems from a lack of belief that people are important to operational results. One particularly uncompromising finance manager in a private hospital described nurses as 'totally replaceable' – and thought they should be paid the minimum that the market would allow. It was difficult to persuade him that their morale or development would adversely affect patient care, the hospital's reputation and ultimately his own operational results.

HOW DO WE CREATE COMMITMENT IN OUR HEALTHCARE ORGANISATIONS?

If you do only one thing to get commitment into your organisation, start measuring your leaders' performance.

Defining, measuring and rewarding good leadership is the key to creating commitment within your organisation. We call this a Leadership Measurement system. This simply means giving every leader a number of targets for key areas and measuring their success at meeting those targets.

I recommend that this be achieved by doing three things:

1. **Give every leader between three and six targets.** There must be at least ONE from each of the Three Circles: operations, patients and people. For instance, a ward leader might have:

- cost against budget
- bed-days
- patient satisfaction
- sickness/absenteeism
- agency shifts

Those targets cover the three key areas (operations, patients, staff) and are simple enough to measure monthly – and if they are not being measured, then they should be. These targets need to be weighted to reflect their importance and the result turned into a percentage. For example, budget may get a 40% weighting and other areas may get 15% each, as a measure of their relative importance. If you hit target in any one area, then you get full marks, or some agreed proportion for coming close – 40 points for coming in on budget (and 35 points for coming close), 15 points for reducing staff absenteeism by 10% and so on. The exact detail needs to be fair and consistent. The points are then added up to give you an overall performance figure for each leader.

2. **Hold each leader to account for these targets every month.** Arrange a system of review which ensures that each manager sits down with each of their leaders for about an hour each month in order to review these numbers and discuss where help and support might be needed.

3. **Publish the results.** Once the system is bedded in, leadership performance needs to be made widely available to staff. This is a strong incentive for people to reach their targets – but it's also a way of engaging the non-

leadership staff in a conversation about performance. Not surprisingly, I've received a lot of resistance to this proposal. Everything from 'The unions won't approve' to 'The whole thing is unfair' to 'Publishing the results would break confidentiality'. All of these have little merit. Holding your leaders to account for performance in their area will give them the commitment that is so sorely needed.

SUPPORTING COMMITMENT – WHAT ELSE YOU WILL NEED TO DO

There are a number of other strategies that work alongside the Leadership Measurement system. These include leadership rounds, talking up and thank-you notes, which were explained in Chapter 4. You will also need to make sure that you are adequately measuring patient and staff satisfaction frequently enough – at least once a month, preferably once a week. I describe two ways of doing this below. All of these things will help you to demonstrate your commitment and to begin to transform your organisation. But I have put them second to leadership measurement, because I firmly believe that measuring your results is the key to that transformation. Numbers have an extraordinary way of focusing the mind and changing behaviour. I will say much more about this in the following chapters.

TELEPHONE FOLLOW-UP

If you are going to hold leaders to account for the way that patients are treated, it is essential that you have a swift and reliable way of understanding what is happening to patients in your hospital. I strongly recommend that all patients are telephoned within 48 hours of being discharged and asked a series of structured questions over 10 minutes. It's a goldmine of immediate information and often identifies who's working hardest and best in your hospital, as the feedback is often positive. It's quick, cheap and easy to implement. It makes patients feel that they are genuinely being cared for, and gives you a chance to find out if they are recovering well. It is also so much more effective than written surveys or surveys done in hospital.

Making these phone calls will initially seem like an enormous task. But implementing a system can be quick – a matter of weeks – providing that senior leaders pursue it with conviction and provide the relevant training and support. This task should be shared among a wide variety of clinical leaders at all levels, whether nurses, doctors, midwives or AHPs. It may seem a lot of extra time and effort, but you can remind doubters that it is only 10 minutes per patient – roughly the same time that an assessment nurse will spend with every A&E attender.

And just in case you don't think this is possible, it's worth bearing in mind that there is a small independent healthcare company in the UK that does it successfully. This company is 'dedicated to a better patient experience' and publishes its patient feedback data and comments on its website every month. Initially, you might think that's a gimmick, or that the organisation would massage its figures. I don't think so. It's like putting the manager's house in the factory. You can't then escape the consequences of poor performance.

STAFF SURVEYS

Similarly, if you are going to hold leaders to account for staff satisfaction, it is essential that you have a reliable way of understanding what is happening to staff. Simple monthly (or even weekly) surveys are easy to implement and far preferable to using indirect methods, such as absenteeism rates. The survey should be short and sweet (five or 10 questions) and should cover the following subjects:

- relationships with peers and leaders
- tools and equipment to do the job
- training and development
- appreciation and acknowledgment

The responses will form the basis of an accurate measure of the ability of leaders to manage their staff effectively.

Again, if you don't think this is possible, I can tell you that I worked with one international pharmacy retail company that asked its staff to complete weekly confidential online surveys of 10 questions that summed up their 'state of mind'. Regional managers and store managers were held to account for the response rate as well as the answers. The company used the results to identify areas that were performing well and those that were at risk of damaging its reputation. The company achieved a top five position in the 'Best Workplace' competition in 2008 and won 'Best Overall Place to Work' in 2009.

CHAPTER 6

Active

'Work together'

Let me tell you about Andy. A great nurse with a huge amount of experience in A&E, Andy has a passion for pain – or, rather, for managing it. I worked with Andy in a private hospital for women and children. Pain was particularly difficult to manage there, as the needs of women in childbirth and of children are, of course, completely different. Andy, though, had volunteered to take on the role of Pain Specialist Nurse. His job was to improve pain management in the hospital.

When I started working with him, Andy was struggling with his role. He knew that good pain management depended on a large number of factors: the anaesthetist, the ward staff, the pharmacists and the clinical leaders all needed to approach the problem together and to do so in a co-ordinated way. He had lots of support, but wasn't getting any results.

The solution was to create a pain management Action Team – a group of motivated staff from different departments and different levels of the organisation: a ward sister, a recovery nurse from theatre, an anaesthetist, an admitting clinician, even a member of the business office. The team met every week; its membership varied over the months, but that didn't matter. Andy was able to use the group to create the momentum that had initially been lacking.

First, the team reviewed and, where necessary, modified the procedures and protocols around pain management, which they then reviewed with the clinical management committee. They then set about changing how expectations were set with patients, how pain was assessed and how it was managed. They organised training for every patient-facing member of staff so that everyone knew how to assess and treat pain effectively.

The other crucial thing they did was to set targets for improvement. As I explained in the opening chapters, numbers provide an opportunity for people to learn and a yardstick by which they can measure their progress. It won't come as a surprise to realise that this is a necessary part of running a successful Action Team. Discussing a problem without measuring progress lacks bite, and people soon drift away. It is important that everyone involved knows that progress will be measured – and how that will be done.

In Andy's case, the hospital used as the yardstick existing feedback on patients' subjective memory of pain – although they put in place proper pain scores for each patient as well. As you can see from the graph, they made a huge impact.

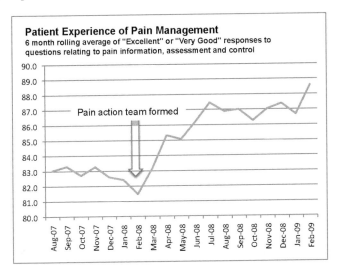

Patient Experience of Pain Management
6 month rolling average of "Excellent" or "Very Good" responses to questions relating to pain information, assessment and control

Pain action team formed

What Andy had hit upon was that in order to tackle a particular problem, he needed three things: a very specific plan of action, collaboration across the organisation and a measurable result.

ACTION VS RESENTMENT

The 2009 swine flu epidemic provided me with an interesting comparison of the different approaches of two hospitals. Both hospitals experienced a doubling of attendances at A&E by worried patients and their families.

In Hospital B, not known for its collaborative approach, the flood of swine flu victims was seen as a burden, purely as extra work. Senior staff used email to give instructions on when and how to judge the necessity of prescribing the anti-viral drugs. This, and other advice, was passed down the line, where staff quickly came to resent what they saw as unnecessary extra work undertaken with little support and even less forethought. Little, apart from the workload, actually changed.

In Hospital A, by contrast, the hospital set up a team to deal with the

---

HOW ORGANISATIONS LEARN

One of the things that Andy learned is that the so-called 'cascade' system doesn't work. It relies on training only the leaders, leaving them to train their deputies, who then train their teams and so on. Most organisations will rely on this – usually for reasons of cost, or a misplaced sense of increasing speed of delivery – but it rarely works. The chain of cascade breaks, thanks to holidays, lack of time or just a lack of motivation to train the next level properly. In Andy's case the lack of training of front-line staff meant that the necessary changes to pain management simply didn't happen.

The fact is – and this is very important in any attempt to change the culture of an organisation – that everyone needs to be dipped in the same stuff. Everyone needs to be trained the same way. This has implications for what we discuss in this chapter (how to hold effective meetings and the importance of team leadership) but it is also crucial to the discussion of leadership in Chapter 8, induction in Chapter 9 and process in Chapter 10.

---

problem, which they called the Swine Flu Emergency Committee. (Personally I don't like the word committee, as it seems too inactive, but no matter.) The team consisted of representatives from all the areas affected, such as A&E, medical nursing, wards, pharmacy and security. The team met every day and tried to solve the problem creatively. They set up a separate swine flu reception, with a patient questionnaire. They changed the traffic flow through the hospital and created a new waiting area. They employed some GPs specifically to deal with the extra patients. After the main surge had passed, which took several days, an email was sent by the COO to every member of staff involved, congratulating and thanking everyone for their contributions. Staff were, needless to say, encouraged.

Was this better leadership or just extra resources? Undoubtedly it was both – along with great management and confident decision-making. The point is that the team approach tackled the problem head-on, spread the load and made decisions more consistent and more visible. This is a superb example of an active organisation.

WHAT IS AN ACTIVE ORGANISATION?

An **active** organisation uses, wherever possible, TEAMS rather than individuals to make decisions.

An **active** organisation is INNOVATIVE – thinking up new, often simple solutions to persistent problems as well as thinking up imaginative ways of tackling new issues.

An **active** organisation is COLLABORATIVE – it tends to use teams that draw their members from many parts of the organisation and from many levels ('cross-functional'), rather than 'functional' teams, the members of which all come from one area or one level.

An **active** organisation is INCLUSIVE – it encourages staff to come up with their own solutions rather than wait for their boss or others to solve things.

An **active** organisation DELIVERS simple solutions to persistent problems.

WHAT'S THE BENEFIT OF ACTION?

Action Teams can solve problems that are not solvable using traditional line management structures. Think about the pain management problem. Everyone is involved in the solution (ward staff, pharmacists, doctors). They don't all report to the same person.

Teams not only outperform but also outlast individuals. When someone in a hierarchy goes on vacation or is ill or moves, the initiatives that they are responsible for will wither or die completely. A team – if well formed and well led – will persist through a fair amount of change and disruption.

Implementation is also much easier, because decisions have come from within the team rather than from on high. And more people know and 'own' the decisions – which makes it much easier to both disseminate and argue the case for any change. 'My boss tells me that...' is much less powerful an argument than 'We all decided that...'

WHAT HAPPENS IF AN ORGANISATION IS NOT ACTIVE?

In an organisation that is not active, there is a reliance on 'command and control', where one person is at the head of all orders and actions. This approach is typical of many healthcare organisations, which traditionally have a hierarchical structure.

However, in most organisations, this structure tends to disenfranchise and disempower people. The result is a 'them and us' attitude, with staff complaining about their superiors – 'them' – as if they weren't all part of a team. Similarly, people will be quick to explain why 'it's not my fault' and give reasons why things 'will never change round here' and why 'it's always been like that'. They feel detached from the organisation and its problems, and feel that these problems can't ever be solved, least of all by them.

Also, where an organisation lacks Action Teams, any problem is seen as a failure of the command and control system, rather than an opportunity for people to get together in a team and start problem-solving. So the first reaction to a problem in an 'inactive' organisation is to try to identify the person or department who 'failed'. It can be very unhealthy.

WHY DON'T WE HAVE ACTION IN OUR HEALTHCARE ORGANISATIONS?

It doesn't sound very difficult, does it? Use teams to implement stuff. People get together, choose a target and then change the way things happen... Well, anyone who has worked in any large organisation will understand that this is the very definition of hard, as I discussed in Chapter 4.

There are a number of reasons why an organisation is not active:

HIERARCHY IS THE PRINCIPAL WAY OF MAKING DECISIONS

We tend to view organisations as organograms, in which people 'report' to other people. This military-style system is useful in some areas, but for complex and wide-ranging changes that cross different departments, it's not appropriate. A hierarchical system believes that 'individuals get stuff done' rather than 'teams outperform individuals'. But we know this isn't so.

NO VALUE IS PLACED ON NON-CLINICAL TIME

'Improvement time' – i.e. time spent off the ward, working out how to improve the organisation – is not valued or even made possible. The pressures of operational targets override the need for thinking time. Time away from the ward or the clinic needs to be recognised and protected – which means that people need to be covered. Given the pressure on rotas, this is often difficult.

But it's a leadership issue. It is essential for a ward leader to understand the importance of a junior member of staff being away from the ward at an Action Team meeting. Senior leaders need to understand this and promote Action Teams and ensure that time off the ward is protected.

JUNIOR STAFF ARE NOT PROPERLY INVOLVED

Action Teams work only if there is a cross-section of people available. Junior staff usually know most about how things actually happen on the ward and in the clinic, and they need to be able to share this knowledge. Improvement teams need to nurture and develop these people – they are an invaluable asset but often lack confidence.

LACK OF A MEASURABLE RESULT

Organisations fail to understand the importance of giving people a way of measuring their progress and therefore tasks are unclear and unfocused.

MEETING INCONTINENCE

Finally – and probably most importantly – the problem with Action Teams is often the meetings. I can't count the number of times I have heard even senior leaders say: 'Oh my God, not another meeting! Why can't we just do something instead of talking about it?' That prompts the question, 'What's so wrong with your meetings?' and I always get the same response: 'We talk and talk and nothing happens. Meetings over-run. No one turns up, or it's cancelled. It's a nightmare!'

The problem is, this is often true. I call it meeting incontinence (which implies incompetence as well as something altogether more unpleasant). It's an inability to hold a meeting together. One of my colleagues in a consulting firm once said that as an implementation consultancy, we probably spent about 50% of our time teaching people how to have good meetings. It's a skill that is badly taught – and usually not taught at all – and this is a real problem. If you're going down the Action Team route, then you need everyone in the team, not just the team leader, to understand how a team meeting should work.

HOW CAN WE CREATE ACTION IN OUR HEALTHCARE ORGANISATIONS?

If you do only one thing to make your organisation more active, teach your staff how to hold effective meetings.

If you ask almost anyone in business – in fact almost anyone at all – whether they enjoy meetings, they will probably squirm. If you encourage them to hold more meetings, rather than fewer, you'll end up with substantial resistance. I know. I've tried it.

The reason that people hate meetings is that meetings tend to be incontinent – or perhaps more charitably, 'ineffective'. Incontinent meetings run on for hours; people go off at tangents, dominate, pontificate, answer their mobile phones, arrive late, leave early... and then the whole thing just peters out.

But – most dishearteningly – people meet and talk without the benefit of numbers and without any numerical targets. Some conversations may not benefit from such a numerical perspective: coaching and counselling, for instance. But most business-related or clinically related conversations should be numbers-based.

When I refer a patient to an on-call physician, I will discuss the patient's history and symptoms, but what the other person needs to know most of all is the numbers: temperature, blood pressure, heart rate. Similarly, there is no point having a meeting about, for instance, patient satisfaction or waiting times, without having some statistics to hand.

So, in any organisation it is essential to teach people how to have effective meetings – and, preferably, more of them. It is essential also for team leaders to learn how to focus a meeting, so that something actually gets done. As suggested above, you'll find that this is always about studying the numbers, which gives the meeting direction and a sense of achievement. You should be asking, where are we numerically, and where do we want to get to?

You also need to teach people how to *attend* meetings – in other words, how to be a useful and effective attendee. Everyone is responsible for meeting continence – not just the team leader.

When I train healthcare teams – or any team, in fact – I encourage them to use meeting effectiveness checklists, which allow teams to assess the meeting according to their own criteria, such as whether the meeting started and ended on time and whether conversations kept to the point. I train people how to focus a meeting on the numbers and I insist that all meetings use action logs, which record what each person agrees to do and can be reviewed at the beginning of the next meeting. With such training and tools, meetings can become continent and from there they can become effective. They may even become popular.

SUPPORTING ACTION – WHAT ELSE YOU WILL NEED TO DO

Organisations have to learn the difficult task of managing by using teams, rather than individuals. It may be difficult at first because there may be a preference for using the more traditional 'command and control' mechanism. Initially, using teams will be more inefficient. However, it's worth the effort. As people become more confident and more competent at running meetings, ideas and projects persist for longer. As a senior leader, this is what you need to do:

1. Select a series of important topics that need cross-functional solutions.
2. Appoint for each topic an Action Team leader. Allow them to select a group of like-minded and enthusiastic people to help them.
3. Train all of them in meeting effectiveness.
4. Protect their time away from their day jobs.
5. Ensure that each team has one and ONLY one target to deliver, and make that target clear and measurable. Make sure each team has a clear plan of how to deliver this target. This plan may need to include putting measurement systems in place.
6. Ask each team to present its plan to the senior management team initially and then every three months to report on its progress.

It is hard to ignore the effect that a good Action Team can have, when you read the swine flu and pain management examples above. But this kind of collaborative behaviour and decisive action occur far too rarely. If you can make such action an integral part of your organisation, it will be a key part of the organisation's transformation.

CHAPTER 7

Responsive

'Listen carefully'

My dad died a few years ago in a hospital in the south-east of England. I have nothing but praise for the staff that looked after him – with one exception.

At one point he was moved from a high-dependency unit to a busy and dysfunctional surgical ward, led by a ward sister who was heard to shout: 'We're not having that head injury in here!' (We'll talk more later about behavioural standards – but this ward could certainly have used some.)

My sister arrived outside visiting hours. She had flown from her home in California, 7,000 miles away, to be with our father, who was desperately ill. She hadn't spent much time with him in the last few years and was worried – rightly – that he was dying.

She arrived a couple of hours before the official two-hour visiting slot and made herself known to the staff, asking if she could sit with her father. One of the nurses point-blank refused: it was out of the question. Rules were rules. My sister had to come back later. After some pleading by my sister, the nurse consulted her senior, who saw sense in allowing her to stay. The nurse, presumably unhappy at being overruled, took my sister into the ward and then left her with the words: 'We tend to remember people like you.'

This – we should not forget – was in 2007, not 1907.

What is going on here? What could possibly be going through the mind of this nurse? What, indeed, is going on in a hospital that restricts visiting hours with such draconian ferocity and refers to patients as 'the head injury' in front of their traumatised families? There are a number of answers, none of which is entirely satisfactory, but it comes down to treating patients as homologous, defined only by their illness or injury, and their families as people to be merely tolerated and controlled rather than listened to.

Such a lack of basic, human, interpersonal, compassionate CARE comes down to an inability to respond to the needs of others. And if we're not good at that in healthcare, we are in quite serious trouble.

THE CUSTOMER IS ALWAYS RIGHT

My view is that to give a poor response to patients and their families when they desperately need our empathy and compassion reveals a lack of customer focus.

I acknowledge that 'customer' is seen as a dirty word by many clinicians, to be ranked up there with 'stakeholders' as meaningless and irrelevant (see 'Is a Patient a Customer?' page 60). But there is a benefit to seeing patients as customers and responding to their needs. Responsiveness has a marked effect on both clinical and financial outcomes; if we do not recognise this, then we are failing not only the patients, but also our shareholders.

Take the example of my father. Would his outcomes have changed markedly if he'd been in a ward where they allowed visitors more freely? Certainly his needs would have been better attended to by his family and better understood, because he couldn't speak properly due to his pain. Maybe if they'd nursed him as Alan (rather than mistaking him for Dennis, no doubt thinking of him as 'the pancreatitis') he might have responded better and not needed a further long stint in Intensive Care after a relapse. Certainly my family would have been more impressed with the hospital had that nurse had more compassion, and the hospital's reputation would have benefited. So the family and patient would have been happier; with a shorter Intensive Care stay, costs would have been reduced; and good feedback from the family would have improved the staff experience. Win, win and win again.

IT HAPPENS TO STAFF, TOO

So the message so far is – respond to your patients. But you must respond to your staff, too. Responsiveness must permeate the entire organisation.

I work in a large hospital, which, like all big organisations, is prone to problems of stock control. Stuff goes missing from store rooms left open on wards. I don't know what the market value of a urinary catheter bag is, but it must be more than zero.

The hospital's response, quite sensibly, is to lock all the store rooms and give responsibility for access to the already overloaded nurse in charge. As a result, all the locks have different combinations – chosen by the ward.

The problem for junior doctors, who work across different wards, comes when a patient becomes unstable, which often happens at night. The doctors need important equipment, and fast. The solution is often to raid the 'crash trolley' where equipment is stored for emergencies. This action, needless to say, is a hanging offence. However, given that nursing staff are thin on the

IS A PATIENT A CUSTOMER?

With good reason, those of us who work in healthcare may baulk at the idea that a patient is a customer. How many customers in any other situation (shops, restaurants, etc.) are sick and frightened when they make their buying decisions? How many 'customers' of healthcare actually understand the decisions that affect their outcome? When we're buying a vehicle we may understand the question of diesel vs petrol. But how many patients understand the question of ciprofloxacin vs erythromycin?

Nonetheless, there are many elements of healthcare that are more like shopping and less like choosing an antibiotic: how we are spoken to, how quickly we are attended to, whether the people we deal with smile and listen. All of these make us feel safer and happier. These should all be performed properly in a healthcare organisation, just as they are in a retail situation.

Many nursing and medical staff persist in seeing patients as a burden, and as a result we 'experts' think we're doing them a favour. This needs to change.

That said, I do recognise why some people in the NHS behave terribly towards their patients. Staff are frequently abused and shouted at by their 'customers' – more so than in John Lewis, you can be sure. They also have to deal with some of the most deprived and dysfunctional people in our society – those with mental illnesses, personality disorders or exceptionally poor behavioural standards.

However, this is no excuse – it's merely a challenge. We can't change this. Abusive individuals are as likely to visit low-cost supermarkets and shops as they are to visit the NHS. Yet the shop staff don't treat their customers any worse than M&S do, even though their market segmentation is different.

ground at night, the alternative would be for the doctor to leave the patient to find someone who knows the code (which will not be one of the many agency nurses working at night), which means faffing around for 30 minutes.

You're the junior doctor. It's your choice: 30 minutes of faffing around while your patient deteriorates or one minute of raiding the crash trolley

---

AND ANOTHER THING...

I was talking to Tom, a senior nurse whose wife is pregnant. At her booking appointment at her local hospital, the couple arrived on time for their appointment and sat with a lot of other pregnant couples in a waiting room. No one explained what they were to do or what was supposed to happen. They had waited for about two hours when a nurse came up to them and led them – without explanation – to another room, where she left them for a further 15 minutes.

A few minutes later a midwife arrived. She said nothing and – again without introduction or explanation – grabbed Tom's wife's arm and took her blood pressure. She asked some questions, gave the expectant mother a small pot in which to provide a urine sample, explaining that she needed to hand that in before leaving, and ushered them back into the waiting room.

We wouldn't expect or allow such treatment of customers from any other profession. Healthcare, in my view, is the last bastion of such poor behaviour.

(with the mental promise that you'll tell the staff or replace the equipment later).

A more sensible solution might be to make the combinations the same on each ward and to make sure that all junior doctors have this common number. Simple and easy to implement? Yes. So why is such a thing not done?

The answer is what links this to my original story about the nurse. The organisation as a whole is not responding (or even listening to) the needs of these members of staff. Plenty of people complained about this problem, but no one did anything about it.

The key to improving such situations, as we shall see, is to create systems within your organisation to ensure that both staff and patients are listened to and responded to.

WHAT IS A RESPONSIVE ORGANISATION?

In short, a responsive organisation recognises and responds to the needs of both customers and staff. In more detail:

A **responsive** organisation LISTENS carefully to its staff and its customers.

A **responsive** organisation CHANGES its systems accordingly.

A **responsive** organisation ADAPTS to the needs of INDIVIDUAL patients and staff.

A **responsive** organisation DEMANDS certain behavioural STANDARDS from its staff.

A **responsive** organisation TRAINS and SUPPORTS staff to provide good customer care.

A **responsive** organisation REWARDS good customer care and improvements.

WHAT IS THE BENEFIT OF RESPONSIVENESS?

The benefits of having a responsive organisation are enormous:

- improved clinical outcomes
- fewer complaints from patients
- happier, more engaged, more productive staff
- reduced staff turnover
- better reputation
- operational savings

How, you might ask, is such an impressive list to be gathered simply from listening and responding properly? How do 'customer service' and 'responding to staff needs' translate into savings and efficiency improvements?

The answer lies in an important psychological principle that underlies much human interaction: *reciprocation*. We respond positively to people who appear to have given something to us. The trust that underpins all trade and commerce relies on the 'I'll give you something if you give me something' idea. It is central to much other human interaction, too. When we feel 'indebted' to someone or some institution, research has shown that we are programmed to 'repay' that debt (see Robert B Cialdini, *Influence: Science and Practice*, Pearson, 2009). We feel benevolent towards people and institutions that provide us with something.

Listening and reacting favourably to patients is clearly beneficial. They will give us the benefit of the doubt, be less likely to sue or complain to us and be more willing to support us in our work, communicate better with us, talk more positively about us to others and so on. In short, responsiveness to patients – what in other circumstances might simply be called 'good customer service' – is a key ingredient of our effectiveness and of our reputation.

Similarly, listening and responding to staff with a degree of empathy and compassion means that the hospital will receive reciprocal behaviour from them, too, because of this sense of indebtedness. People are more likely to continue working for an organisation that listens and responds to them.

Where staff are listened and responded to, they will more happily put in the discretionary effort necessary to deliver the clinical and process improvements that we will discuss in Chapter 10. And if staff are more well-disposed towards the organisation, they are less likely to leave it and more likely to speak well of it to outsiders.

Given the right opportunities and the right environment, your staff will strive to do things right first time, every time, for every patient. Clinical outcomes improve, patients are happier, staff experience improves, money is saved. So healthcare organisations must create an environment where staff want to change the way they work and collaborate in new ways – to develop real ownership for the performance of the organisation.

WHAT HAPPENS IF AN ORGANISATION IS NOT RESPONSIVE?

It's not difficult to see that without responsiveness it is easy for an organisation to lose its patients and staff – both literally and metaphorically.

I am reminded constantly in my work with clients and as an employee by examples of how *not* to be responsive. I saw one such example at a new-build hospital at which I worked, where staff had submitted a written petition asking for an on-call staff room. (Staff really mean business when they start producing written petitions.) Despite their efforts, the leadership team delivered to every member of staff a long letter explaining all the myriad reasons why a staff room was both unnecessary and, I quote, 'impossible'. Was space so much at a premium? Were working patterns so very different? Perhaps. But the impact on staff was to make them believe that their leaders cared not for their opinions or desires. Turnover, sickness and absenteeism remain a problem at that hospital.

What about the long-suffering patients and their families? What's the impact of our failure to respond to them, and to treat them with the compassion and the individuality that they need? The most likely reaction is, of course, fear and anxiety. People fear hospitals. They are anxious because they don't know what is going to happen to them and their loved ones. It is well-proven that anxiety increases pain and the length of a hospital stay and worsens clinical outcomes.

But the other more likely reaction of patients is anger. In my family's example, my sister would have happily murdered the nurse in question. That nurse's behaviour overshadowed our otherwise excellent experience of the care my father had received, and undermined the efforts of so many other people in the organisation. That one nurse cost the hospital its reputation. (I will talk more about how to deal with such negative attitudes in Chapter 9.)

As it was, we sent the hospital a letter explaining our concerns and received a lovely phone call from the chief nurse that lasted around 15 minutes. She assured us that the nurse had already been identified and removed.

A good response – but is this something that the chief nurse should be doing? How much time does she spend ringing hurt relatives and otherwise dealing with complaints such as this? A day a month? A day a fortnight? Possibly more, if my clients are to be believed. Her phone call wouldn't have been necessary had the first nurse done a better job, so her time was being wasted. If they had implemented the telephone follow-up system that I recommend in Chapter 5, our complaint would have been dealt with more swiftly – before resentment built up and before we had lodged a formal complaint.

It's not hard to see how efficient systems and processes can be subsumed by poor customer service and by poor care for staff – by poor responsiveness throughout the organisation.

There is a further point to make about how we respond to patients. At one hospital in which I work, in an area renowned for its knife crime, the receptionists sit at an open, low-level desk – just the right height to be shouted at or stabbed. But they're not. I have never seen any violence towards staff in that hospital, despite its location. In one of my previous hospitals, by contrast, receptionists sat behind bullet-proof glass. The result? Frequent acts of aggression and verbal assault. A dangerous atmosphere pervades the place. If we treat our patients with fear and suspicion, we will inevitably reap what we sow.

WHY DON'T WE HAVE RESPONSIVENESS IN OUR HEALTHCARE ORGANISATIONS?

It's worth asking ourselves why we don't have great responsiveness in our healthcare institutions. Why don't we treat patients like valued customers, as the best retailers do? Why don't we treat our staff like the valuable, knowledgeable and committed people that they are? I have a number of thoughts about this.

THE MONOPOLY/OLIGOPOLY OF THE NHS AND PRIVATE CARE

If you are treated badly in a shop or restaurant, you just go elsewhere. By contrast, in healthcare, you can't easily choose another nurse, or even another hospital, whatever the politicians may hope for. This applies to staff as well as patients. The market for healthcare is by no means perfect. So, no one feels the need to provide good customer service. The patients will turn up anyway, won't they?

THE CULTURE CAN BE TO TREAT PATIENTS POORLY

In some places it is the norm to complain about patients and treat them as a nuisance. In such places it is hard for individuals to buck this trend. Seeing patients as a nuisance becomes part of the culture, and 'good service' can become a cultural anathema, as if treating patients well were unnecessary,

---

TREAT THEM MEAN...

I went into hospital for an operation on my ankle a couple of years ago. It was Christmas Eve and I arrived with a number of other patients at a darkened ward. We waited around for a while, wondering if we were in the right place. Suddenly a member of staff burst in and started barking at us that we were all going to have to be patient because they were short-staffed. Only she had come to work, and it would take a long time for her to check us all in.

I don't know what my fellow patients felt, but even I was slightly spooked that maybe there wouldn't be enough staff in theatres. How many recovery nurses would there be? Everyone felt at best unwanted and at worst quite anxious, both of which were completely unnecessary.

---

even pointless. It requires strong and consistent leadership to change this way of thinking (which we will discuss in the next chapter).

STAFF OFTEN FIND IT HARD TO MAKE A DIFFERENCE

I resist the over-used term 'disempowered' but the gist is the same. If your systems and processes don't work, or you are truly understaffed, then it's hard to provide great service. Staff lose heart, and there is no chance of their developing performance ownership.

IT'S EASIER TO BE DEAF

Listening to both our patients and staff can at first be a depressing experience. It can feel as if we're just making more work for ourselves. Remaining deaf seems preferable.

THERE ARE TOO FEW MEASURES AND NO STANDARDS

We don't measure the effectiveness of our customer care or our staff satisfaction enough. This is slowly changing with the advent of the 'patient experience' as a government priority, but there are, as yet, no national 'standards' or guidelines, and few even at institutional level. Staff experience measures are even further behind. So no one knows how well or badly they're doing, nor can they be properly encouraged to do better.

STAFF HAVE NO DIRECT INCENTIVE TO PROVIDE GREAT CUSTOMER CARE

Busy days are just that. Busy. They don't provide any more data or any more money for the people actually providing the care.

THERE IS OFTEN TOO LITTLE COMPASSION BETWEEN STAFF

This is possibly the most important point. If we don't treat each other, as staff, with the courtesy and compassion that we all expect, it is harder for staff to feel compassionate towards patients. Being pressured by your boss is one thing (and challenge is important), but being reprimanded at every opportunity is quite another. Management has to be effective *and* compassionate.

THE PSYCHOLOGY OF SERVICE IS POORLY UNDERSTOOD

We don't teach clinicians or our allied staff anything about providing good customer service. We think this is for retail and other sectors. Theory and good practice abound, but the healthcare industry seems reluctant to embrace this (see 'Is a Patient a Customer?' page 60). For healthcare staff to see patients as customers and learn to treat them as such is a huge but necessary culture change, and staff do need to be properly trained for this to happen.

HOW CAN WE CREATE RESPONSIVENESS IN OUR HEALTHCARE ORGANISATIONS?

The most important thing you can do to make your organisation more responsive is to introduce behavioural guidelines and 'Do Say, Don't Say'.

Is your healthcare organisation a model of respect between staff and patients? What about between staff and staff? In many well-run hospitals the answer will be yes, but I have worked with hospitals where this is not the case. In the worst cases, senior staff shout at their juniors at the slightest provocation. But there can be other, less dramatic, everyday problems, such as discourtesy, lack of punctuality, carelessness and so on. I advise my clients to develop a set of behavioural standards that apply across the organisation at every level and that govern all behaviour – between staff and patients, but also among the staff themselves. Each organisation should create its own appropriate standards; I give an example here that was created by one of my clients, which they gave the acronym RESPECT.

R = Relaxed. Do not raise your voice; remain calm and composed.

E = Eye contact. Make eye contact with people when you talk to them.

S = Smile (it's free).

P = Polite: be courteous, address people with their title and surname until they say otherwise; if people are lost, show them the way.

E = Enthusiasm. Be positive and helpful with your colleagues and patients. Offer help and thanks willingly.

C = Confidential. Never discuss patients where you can be overheard or outside the hospital. Never disclose personal information about patients.

T = Timely. Be on time; don't keep staff or patients waiting; if there's a delay, explain it; give people an estimate of how long something will take.

ACT LOCAL

I advise also that all departments create their own sets of rules about how to engage with patients. We call these 'Do Say, Don't Say' guidelines, and they help staff to explain everyday issues and problems to patients in a positive and courteous way. Healthcare is too complicated for scripting, but some ways of saying things are better than others.

For example, instead of telling a patient: 'We're short-staffed, you'll have to wait,' it would be better to say: 'There are priority patients that we need to see first. We will probably be able to see you within the hour; if you need anything in the meantime, please ask the nurse at reception.'

The most important thing to stress here is that the guidelines should be produced by the people who have to adhere to them and NOT given to them by their managers or by people 'on high'. Also, they must be guidelines and not a script – scripted responses are obviously fake and not at all reassuring.

The most important thing to do, in fact, is to bring 'customer service' into open discussion. Most people embrace the idea of doing and saying the right thing to patients and are glad of some help in defining what 'the right thing' might be. (Some will, obviously, sneer at the idea, but we'll come to them later in Chapter 9.) In particular, by introducing the two measures described above, you are telling your staff that customer service is a vital part of the hospital's culture.

SUPPORTING RESPONSIVENESS: WHAT ELSE YOU WILL NEED TO DO

As well as the suggestions above, the leadership rounds and thank-you notes described in Chapter 4 will help to make your organisation more responsive by listening to and bolstering the confidence of staff. The active and visible support of leaders using simple methods of reward and recognition quickly makes a difference.

There are a number of other things that will help.

SIMPLE 'CUSTOMER SERVICE' TRAINING FOR ALL STAFF

This needn't be extensive and should be pitched as 'getting the best out of your relationship with patients' – rather than (as I have seen it) a sort of remedial detention full of exhortations to smile. I teach my clients a simple six-step process called 'GUIDES'. It takes no more than half an hour to learn because it is so simple.

Greet: Acknowledge the person by their name.

Understand: Make sure you and they understand what you're saying. Can they hear you? Do they speak English? Many times I've heard people give long explanations to demented patients when they would have done better speaking to the relatives.

Introduce: Tell them who you are and what your role is (patients don't know what your uniform means).

Duration: Tell them how much of their time you are asking for (whether for an activity or a wait).

Explain: Tell them what you're going to do before you do it – and why.

Sign off: Say goodbye, use their name again and make it clear that you're going. If possible, tell them what will happen next.

PROPER HANDLING OF COMPLIMENTS

Hospitals normally have extensive systems for dealing with complaints from patients. But how many of them have effective ways of feeding back compliments to staff? I recently received a card from a patient thanking the whole A&E department for a job well done. I was told by one of the consultants to pin it to the board in the staff room. But it's not measured or managed properly under those circumstances. Staff who have contributed need to be properly commended – it's not difficult and it has a huge impact on behaviour.

DEALING EFFECTIVELY WITH COMPLAINTS

Complaints must be dealt with swiftly and effectively. Our family's experience of being telephoned by the chief nurse really worked for us. By contrast, one hospital I worked in asked me to comment on a complaint seven months after they had received it. I was more embarrassed by the slowness of their response than by the original clinical issue. I have no idea what the patient thought, but I doubt they will speak kindly of the hospital. My solution to complaint handling is to measure both compliments and complaints and to publish these two side by side down to the ward and department level.

TRAINING IN HOW TO DEAL WITH CONFRONTATION

First-level leaders (ward sisters and department heads) and front-line staff often have to deal with irate and unhappy patients or their families. We know a lot about that in A&E. Often this is caused by frustration with poor service, but it's also about the fear and anxiety that goes with being a patient. There are good ways and bad ways of dealing with these situations, and most people would benefit from some training in confrontation and dealing with aggression, to help them to diffuse tension rather than exacerbate it.

TELEPHONE FOLLOW-UP

This was explained in Chapter 5, but is repeated here because it is an essential element of understanding the patient experience. In addition, it works much more rapidly than written patient surveys.

PATIENT FORUMS

A lot of hospitals have these, and many have a PALS service, which could help. As a way of listening to the patient's experience, they work only if the staff running them can be sure that their ideas will turn into action. This means that the patient forum needs to be seen as an Action Team (see Chapter 6) rather than a committee or talking-shop.

STAFF FORUMS

One leader told me that staff forums were merely a means for people to 'waste time getting together to whinge about work'. My response to this is twofold. You need to have good meeting leadership (we cover this in Chapter 10) and you need to have good monitoring and recording of staff issues, which are always followed up between meetings.

STAFF SURVEYS

These were explained in Chapter 5; in this context, they help to show your staff that you are listening and that you need and value their input.

CHAPTER 8

Energetic

'Give support'

Moving a hospital is a tricky business. As you can imagine, it takes months of planning and an extraordinary amount of effort in addition to the day-to-day business of running an already complicated organisation. A few years ago, I was working in a hospital that had just built a brand new state-of-the-art facility at the cost of many millions of pounds. One Friday evening, the doors to the old A&E department closed and the entire staff were brought in to move all the equipment, beds, tubes, lights, drugs and everything else from one building to another. The move went without a hitch and the new emergency department and ward were re-opened on Monday morning. It was a very successful exercise.

I was talking to the person in charge of that move the other day. We were discussing leadership. He looked at me and shook his head. The only thing that saddened him about that move, he said, was that not one of the members of the hospital leadership team had taken the time to visit the new department during or after the move to congratulate them on a job well done. The success of the new hospital had been assured by the staff's hard work, but no one had bothered to thank them for their efforts. The result was predictable. Negative stories started to circulate about how the staff were taken for granted – about how all the money had been spent on fancy new equipment rather than more staff or better salaries. It was a truly wasted opportunity to enthuse the staff about their new department.

Fast forward a few years. In the same A&E department one of the senior consultants stormed into the busy waiting room, packed with people who, in his opinion, should have been making appointments with their GP rather than coming to an emergency department. In a loud voice he announced to a bemused collection of patients: 'Listen up, people. If you're not dead, leave!' He wasn't joking. He was frustrated. Frustrated by the lack of support and resources provided for the tide of primary care patients arriving in his emergency department. And we should not forget: treating coughs and colds in A&E is ludicrously expensive.

Like most people, the junior members of staff found the consultant's outburst funny, and they tell the story to each other. The juniors, seeing their boss act this way, tend to adopt some of his frustrated attitude. And this attitude to patients rubs off in subtle ways: this is, for instance, the only place I know of where staff refer to patients as a matter of course by their condition (e.g. 'the laceration in cubicle 9') rather than by their name. Eventually, negativity spreads and the effect is to demotivate and depress staff throughout the department.

In both these cases we are witnessing something of overriding importance to every organisation. It is 'the shadow of the leader'. The distance between the senior managers and the department casts a shadow over the clinical leaders. The frustration of those clinical leaders casts a shadow over those treating the patients.

Yet none of this is in any way malicious. In fact it is unlikely that any of these leaders has considered the impact that their behaviour has on the performance of their department or on the hospital. I would hazard – particularly in the case of the consultant – that this is largely because little emphasis has been placed on the importance of leadership and leadership behaviour.

Doctors are very thoroughly schooled and tested in the arts and science of medicine. They are not let loose on patients without some very rigorous training. But we allow the same doctors to lead the departments of a complex organisation with very little training or support in the art and science of leadership. Yet poor leadership can be devastating to an organisation, just as good leadership can transform it.

INSPIRATION IN ACTION

I want to contrast this situation with one that I know personally from my leadership development and coaching work. Mark and Amelia are leaders of a group of consultants within a large accountancy company. In contrast to much of what happens in healthcare, their work advising companies is, if you ask me, studiously dull. At root, it appears to be just spreadsheets and meetings. It may involve giving high-level advice to important people, but however you cut it, much of the daily grind must be mind-numbing.

Both Mark and Amelia are intelligent, articulate and hardworking. They have a very clear vision of where they want their business to go. In just three years, they have grown their group of consultants from just the two of them to 65 people and driven revenues to the point that their practice is one of the highest-earning within a global business of 125,000 employees.

I wouldn't suggest that these two individuals are perfect. They have their faults like the rest of us. But there is no doubt that their staff love working for them. As leaders, they constantly provide context by reminding their team how they are re-shaping the way that businesses are run – and in so doing are having an impact on the way that business in general is done. They articulate this 'first or best' position with real clarity. They give their staff incentives and opportunities for self-development and provide support and encouragement. They give praise and recognition where it is due and they provide challenge where appropriate.

As a result, the atmosphere among the team is extraordinary. The young men and women are excited about their work. They talk with enthusiasm about their projects and their clients. Without doubt they have performance ownership in spades. They stand out from their colleagues in other teams as bright-eyed and ambitious. They are, in short, inspired. And there is no doubt that this is due to their leaders – and the shadow of their leadership.

This is the subject of this chapter. It is about how leaders behave and how that behaviour can energise or demotivate the people around them. It is also about how we can and must train leaders to be more like Amelia and Mark and less like our frustrated clinician. Some people are natural leaders; most are not. But most people can be taught leadership as a skill, to great effect. (And even 'natural leaders' can always learn something new.) We must value leadership excellence as highly as we do clinical excellence.

We need to recognise also that leadership is a subject that applies to leaders at all levels – whether they are boardroom 'C-level' executives or 'shop-floor' matrons, registrars, supervisors and sisters. It applies also to the people who have no formal role as leaders but who nevertheless influence those around them.

I have emphasised energy in this chapter because that is the outcome of good leadership. We want positive, motivated and capable staff who are fully engaged in the task of patient care and who work well with each other. This is all possible if the leadership in an organisation is energetic. In Chapter 7 we talked about listening and responding. This is the next step – leaders must truly lead.

LEADERSHIP VS MANAGEMENT

A wealth of literature and Herculean amounts of research exist on the subject of leadership. Despite this, healthcare professionals tend to talk about 'management' rather than 'leadership'. Most administrators that we work with have 'manager' in their title, and I have found that very few think of themselves as 'leaders'.

When I run seminars on leadership, I discuss the idea of 'management' and how the term implies control, process, problem-solving, submission and rules. I contrast this with 'leadership' and its suggestion of inspiration, creativity and empowerment. Our seminar attendees understand the difference between these two ideas very well, and recognise that there is a need for both. What is sad is that many of them don't feel like leaders and so don't behave as such. I regularly find that 'managers' in healthcare – especially those on the front line – rarely allow themselves to feel and act like leaders. Their jobs are so often about 'managing' – in the sense of 'getting by' – that there often seems little room for anything but fire-fighting.

It is largely for this reason that I have tried to focus this chapter on the energy that is created by good leaders and on the emotional effect of good and bad leadership, rather than on the technicalities of its definition or its relationship to management.

WHAT IS AN ENERGETIC ORGANISATION?

An **energetic** organisation INSPIRES its staff.

An **energetic** organisation is a POSITIVE place to work.

An **energetic** organisation DEVELOPS and SUPPORTS its staff and leaders.

An **energetic** organisation implements CHANGE easily.

An **energetic** organisation has MINDFUL leaders who have positive IMPACT.

WHAT'S THE BENEFIT OF ENERGY?

With enough energy, an organisation can move mountains. With it, we can:

- improve staff motivation and morale
- provide better patient care
- use resources more effectively

Energy also makes change easier, which is clearly important if you are setting out to transform an organisation. Why is this? Making changes and improvements to an organisation requires discretionary effort. Staff must be willing to extend themselves beyond their job description; they must care

---

TRAINING THE LEADERS

The British Army has long realised that if you're going to inspire people to decisive action in difficult circumstances, then you need good leaders.

To become an army officer, you must first pass through initial officer training at the Royal Military Academy Sandhurst. The objective, they say, is 'to foster the attributes of intellect and character, which, combined with development of professional competence, equip the officer for the responsibilities of leadership on first appointment'.

I draw your attention to those last two words. First appointment. The army steeps its leaders in at least six months of training before it allows any of them into a position of leadership. Sandhurst also sees leadership as being dependent not only on professional competence but also on 'intellect and character'.

None of our healthcare leaders is privileged enough to be trained with anything like the intensity or academic quality that is found at Sandhurst. This is our loss. Inadequate leadership in healthcare may not be as catastrophic as having a poorly led army, but I would suggest it is a more general hazard and certainly not of 'low risk'.

---

about making things better for their patients and colleagues. If that is to happen, staff need someone to inspire, motivate and encourage them to make something of their daily opportunities. This takes energy.

WHAT HAPPENS IF AN ORGANISATION LACKS ENERGY?
In an organisation that lacks energy, you will find:
- low morale
- stagnation
- loss of direction
- poor teamwork
- negative culture
- high staff turnover

This last point is important. In a stagnating organisation, the good people leave. Research shows that the main reason for leaving a job is not conditions, pay or the promise of better things elsewhere. It is that the employee doesn't like working for his or her team leader. People leave their boss, not their job.

Recent research shows that 60% of all employees think they could do a better job without their immediate boss. Such bosses are clearly lacking in something. Unless we can do something about this, we will have to learn to live with high staff turnover, not to mention the many other depressing effects of poor leadership that we've discussed.

HIDDEN AMBITIONS
I once worked for a large multinational where one of the senior leaders – let's call him John – made it clear that he was just waiting out his tenure. He saw no point in hiding it. He had about three years to go before retirement. His department was a shambles and he'd lost any motivation to change.

Before you rush to blame him, however, I should point out that he had been promoted to this position many years ago and since then had received not one day of development. Not one day of training, not one hour of coaching. When we started working with him, he was resistant to any change. At one point, he accused us of 'meddling' with his department. But he was a thoughtful man and soon realised that he could learn something, which invigorated him. Not only did we improve the performance statistics of his department, but also we parted firm friends.

This taught me something. Nearly everyone wants to become a better leader. I know from experience that people respond positively to organisations that encourage their development. They don't want to be patronised, and many may resist the idea of 'leadership training' at first, but almost all will take to it eventually. And, of course, all will benefit enormously – as will their staff.

WHY DON'T WE HAVE ENERGY IN OUR HEALTHCARE ORGANISATIONS?

Generating energy is – as the metaphor would suggest – a continual effort. Leaders must work constantly to create the right levels of enthusiasm, and this takes capability and enthusiasm on their part. So perhaps it's not surprising that there are many reasons why organisations lack this vital energy.

LEADERSHIP TRAINING IS NOT SEEN AS COST-EFFECTIVE

Leaders receive very little development mainly because of the view that 'leadership' is something to do with HR rather than a core element of the organisation. Leadership seems to many to have no measurable impact on operations. And because the impact is hidden, the received wisdom is that development has no clear cost benefit. Not so. Put simply, it costs considerably less to train someone than it does to recruit them. So if training reduces churn, which it does, the financial benefit to an organisation is obvious.

LEADERSHIP TRAINING TENDS TO BE ABOUT MANAGEMENT

Leadership is about generating energy, about inspiring others. But a lot of training for leaders is geared towards 'getting things right', rather than 'doing the right thing'; in other words, managing rather than leading. Training someone in process doesn't change leadership behaviour.

LEADERS DON'T KNOW WHAT THEY DON'T KNOW

I have worked with many organisations over the years and in many of them I've run leadership courses. In almost all of them the senior leaders refuse to attend, using a variety of excuses. Some are embarrassed to attend training with people who are their 'juniors'. Some think they're too busy (for which, read 'too important'), which is, in my experience, a very bad sign. They make the mistake of thinking that leadership can't be taught and that their skills are adequate. They are wrong on both counts.

THERE IS OFTEN NO LONG-TERM VIEW

Energising an organisation not only takes effort, but also takes a very long time. Most senior leaders are in their posts for a maximum of three years. Many are in and out of the top job within 18 months. They want to see immediate results, and teaching leaders how to inspire their staff is not a quick win. It may sound cynical, but while leadership development sounds good, it doesn't deliver quickly.

ENERGY MUST BE DEMONSTRATED BUT RARELY IS

Good leadership is in quite short supply, it seems. I once asked a delegate on a course if they had experience of coaching. 'One of my bosses used to take us all into his office every Friday and shout at us,' he said. I often ask attendees to describe the most inspiring leader they've worked for. Many people resort, after considerable thought, to saying 'my mother'. If you've never had an inspiring and energising boss, you'll have difficulty acting in an inspiring manner. Leadership – and inspiring leadership – can be taught. It's just more difficult in the absence of a good model.

HOW DO WE CREATE ENERGY IN OUR HEALTHCARE ORGANISATIONS?

If you do only one thing to create energy in your organisation, introduce a sustainable leadership programme.

As I have said before, what leaders want, and many need, is a comprehensive introduction to the art and science of leadership. We recommend that every leader is introduced to the very basics of leadership. I run a four-day course as a starter, which runs over consecutive days or across several weeks, depending on the needs of the organisation. It covers four main themes:

- Leading Self: how understanding yourself can help (includes **mindfulness** – see opposite)
- Leading Others: influencing others (includes **impact** – see page 82)
- Leading Teams: theory and practice of team development (includes **coaching** – see page 83)
- Leading for Results: introduction to systems and processes

By the way, if you run a course of this kind, every member of the board and everyone with any leadership responsibility should attend. (That includes the housekeeping supervisors whose first language may not be English, as much as it includes the board and the execs.) It especially includes the people who think they have an excuse for not attending.

However, this is only the start. To make the right behaviour stick, we need to convert the initial enthusiasm for this sort of work into something sustainable. That's what leadership academies are for.

SUPPORTING ENERGY – WHAT ELSE YOU WILL NEED TO DO

LEADERSHIP ACADEMIES

I strongly recommend setting up your own 'leadership academies' within your organisation. These are leadership training schemes geared towards your particular hospital and your staff. I recommend, as discussed, that everyone with any leadership responsibilities attend, and that you set aside at least one day every quarter – preferably two – for leadership work. This can include guest speakers, case studies, days with themes, even days out.

The point of this is to demonstrate that leadership skills need to be refreshed regularly and sustained. Many organisations run, or send their employees on, occasional courses, assuming that one hit will do the trick. But leadership is a continual learning experience.

The other point to make is that a leadership academy must be owned by the people who are organising it. If this kind of training is imposed from outside, it is never going to last – it will seem too much like school. Putting it at the heart of an organisation is the key to making this a positive and relevant experience for all leaders and thereby to generating more energy.

On a personal note, I have a suspicion of some 'leadership development' activity – the kind that involves making people run around outdoors or indulge in competitive projects that have little relevance to their working environment. Roping barrels together to make a raft or paintballing can be fun – and can help to build relationships – but I've not found anything of this sort that makes a lasting difference to leadership capability.

MINDFUL LEADERSHIP

One of the principal things that I teach leaders is the importance of self-awareness – which simply means understanding how you react to situations and people, so that you can modify those reactions if you see fit. If you are self-aware, you can practise what I call MINDFUL leadership.

The concept of mindfulness comes out of meditation practices and helps people to become more in tune with the way they think and with the way their prejudices or assumptions can affect their behaviour. A mindful leader, for example, would not storm into A&E and have an outburst, because he would be too aware of the impact that his behaviour would have; he would also not see all patients as nuisances, cluttering up his A&E department, because he would not succumb to that prejudice. Similarly, a mindful leader would have gone to visit the new A&E department, set up by his hard-working staff. He would have been instinctively aware of the need for his involvement in that exceptional effort.

Mindfulness is too extensive a subject to cover here; if you are interested in pursuing it further, the key place in the UK for academic study of the subject is the Centre for Mindfulness Research and Practice at Bangor University.

THE IMPACT OF IMPACT

I recently saw a senior member of the Department of Health give a talk at a conference. At the end of his 30 minutes, I had very little idea what he had been trying to say. I remembered none of it and was certainly none the wiser. I wasn't alone. The people around me had resorted to playing with their mobile phones, texting, doodling or looking through the catalogue. A little while later, on the same stage, a young exec held the audience spellbound with a riveting and entertaining account of a little device that he'd designed. It's a shame, because the senior civil servant was probably trying to tell us something of great import. But he missed his chance. He needed some IMPACT training.

The concept of IMPACT is simply this: How do you make an impact with others? How come some people are better at it than others? How can you learn to make your impact positive? Generating a positive impact – and therefore creating ENERGY – needs a level of self-awareness and MINDFULNESS. All leaders obviously need to make a positive impact on their staff, and it is something that can be taught.

I came across the concept of IMPACT training through a colleague, Noa Maxwell, who teaches the subject. Most of the time, I reckon I have a reasonable bedside manner. But I was less confident about how I came across in sales meetings and when presenting at conferences. Noa taught me about pauses, about listening, and about being genuine and unscripted in my conversations. He showed me, quite literally, by using a video camera to record my performance.

When I watched myself on video it was excruciating, but at least after that I didn't have to imagine what I looked like. I was able to both see and hear myself more clearly. With Noa's help I've improved my own impact. And I recommend this technique to all my clients. It can be fun, and it teaches us more in a few minutes than we might otherwise learn in many years.

COACHING

In the past, coaching has been over-hyped as a panacea. I do think it's important, but it won't solve all your problems. What it can do is allow leaders to help unlock a team member's assumptions about their own work. For instance, I once coached a woman who had some very restricted ideas about her own authority – she felt she had no impact on the people senior to her. She was stuck in the command and control paradigm. By exploring with me the idea that the people 'above' her would listen to her and take notice of her opinions, she came to realise that she had more power to influence senior people than she realised. This one conversation transformed her behaviour overnight.

BUDDY PROGRAMMES

Buddy programmes are a useful idea that I recommend. In a buddy system, individuals pair up to give each other mutual support in their everyday work. I've found in the past that this system helps to create a sense of cohesion and build confidence among leaders. As an example, I worked on a leadership training programme with one first-level leader who had a junior role in a busy operating theatre department. He was quite introverted and lacked confidence. Having spent years without any support, he found his buddy relationship incredibly valuable and became a much more outgoing and useful member of the department. His feedback was that it was 'of great use to me personally, in my growth as a leader... I feel I have grown in stature and have changed the way I have approached challenges.' I find that buddy programmes can be a great adjunct to a leadership programme.

IMPACT TRAINING

I've mentioned impact already as a general skill (see The Impact of Impact, opposite), but it's of particular relevance to senior individuals, who will often have little time to get their message across. Getting senior leaders to engage their staff isn't difficult. It's often just a matter of spending a few hours with them, showing them how to come across as genuine and passionate – something they can probably do among friends, but don't give themselves permission to do at work. Impact training can help enormously with this.

MINDFULNESS COURSES

I encourage mindfulness training for clients (see 'Mindful Leadership', page 81). Learning to absorb and process information about their organisation in different ways can help leaders to see the wood rather than the trees. Some people take to it, some don't, but it is worth a try to get a completely new perspective on work and one's role in an organisation.

CHAPTER 9

Focused

'Be fearless'

We talked in Chapter 5 about the need for commitment in an organisation. I suggested that we could improve performance by making sure all leaders were given balanced targets and were encouraged to behave in ways that proved their commitment to those targets.

In the three chapters that followed – Active, Responsive, Energetic – we learned something of the skills needed to lead an organisation towards improved performance. By contrast, the next two chapters – Focused and Uniform – are about transformation, rather than mere improvement. They are about taking the organisation to a whole new level: a better place for both patients and staff.

A word of warning. I'm tempted to stick a notice on this chapter that says: 'Please don't try this at home'. The ideas and techniques in these chapters require that your organisation has already been through the first few stages of the CAREFUL programme. Your organisation needs excellent problem-solving skills (Active), a focus on service (Responsive) and good leadership training (Energetic) before you go to the next stage.

WHAT LEVEL OF FAILURE IS ACCEPTABLE?

I occasionally do leadership development and coaching work in a successful independent hospital. It's successful because it turns in good financial performance year after year and has reasonably good patient and staff satisfaction figures. The CEO is savvy and capable, but after many years in the game she is also prone to cynicism not just about 'her' doctors but also about staff and patients. A conversation between us when we first started working together turned to the subject of patient complaints. The question was: what was an acceptable level of complaints? 'Obviously,' I said, 'the target should be zero.'

'Nonsense!' she said, becoming agitated. 'We'll always get complaints. That's the nature of our patients. They're the complaining sort. Many of them deliberately make problems so that they can get a reduction on their bill.'

As I considered this, I was struck by two things. First, if the CEO has such a low opinion of her patients, does the shadow of her leadership fall across the organisation? As I continued to work there, I discovered that the answer was yes. The view that patients were problematic ran deep. Any sort of grumble by a patient immediately labelled them as 'difficult', which put up barriers between them and the staff. 'Oh,' staff would say, 'Mrs Jones is a troublemaker.' Even if Mrs Jones was in pain, frightened or simply cold, any request or comment was thenceforth met with suspicion and defensiveness.

The second thing that struck me was that, if the answer to the question was not zero, then it was difficult to know what number of complaints was acceptable. If one patient in a hundred complained, was that OK? What about two out of a hundred? How about 20? The answer this hospital used was: 'Fewer than last year.'

It's worth comparing this situation to what has happened in manufacturing in the last few decades. These days – unlike, say, 30 years ago – we don't expect to take an expensive piece of electronic gadgetry out of its box and find that it doesn't work. Or that the instructions are missing. Or that the box contains the wrong item. The number of manufacturing errors that reach the customer for most high-value goods is like the number of unsafe incidents at DuPont – as close to zero as is possible to measure.

Of course, things do go wrong occasionally, even with high-value goods. A friend of mine recently bought a new German-made car on which the steering lock broke after a few weeks. One phone call to the sales company brought an engineer to the car within hours. Within two days the car had been driven back to the garage, repaired and returned to the owner, washed and valeted. At no point did anyone give the impression that demanding purchasers of high-value automobiles are the complaining type.

Going into hospital – whether funded by the government, an insurance company or by your savings – is an expensive business. In many cases, more expensive than a new car. And yet, in my experience, the people providing this service believe that complaints are unavoidable. There is a culture that says healthcare staff should not go out of their way to prevent complaints occurring, but should use their energy to avoid any admission that something might be wrong. Complaints are seen as inevitable, and therefore meaningless, rather than an indication that something is wrong and ought to be fixed.

How did the transformation in manufacturing take place? How did we get from a point where 'Made in Japan' was synonymous for shoddy manufacture to a point where Far Eastern manufacturers have almost wiped out much of the European and US manufacturing industry? There are many factors – some macroeconomic, some political, some cultural – but there is no doubt it could not have happened if those manufacturers had taken the view that their customers were too demanding or that mistakes are bound to happen.

BREAKTHROUGH ATTITUDES, BREAKTHROUGH RESULTS

In Chapter 5, I talked about DuPont and its commitment to safety. I explained that the company made safety a measurable target for every leader and impressed on every employee that safety was their concern. What I didn't emphasise was its obsession with the idea of zero accidents and zero harm.

To get to a point of zero complaints – or zero defects in manufacturing your mobile phone, or zero accidents in a munitions factory – we need an attitude of positive engagement from everyone in the organisation, from the board room to the ward. The senior leadership must stake their reputation on making that happen. Any suggestion that 'things just happen' or 'complaints are inevitable' must be eradicated.

I call these 'breakthrough attitudes' – the ability to imagine and then pursue a world where zero errors is the right answer. Breakthrough attitudes require leaders to use imagination and courage. Leaders need to summon all their powers of impact and persuasion to inspire people to pursue seemingly impossible targets.

Breakthrough attitudes require people to have a sense of space, of freedom of action, of responsiveness, of energy. They require people to be inclusive, positive and compassionate. Above all, breakthrough attitudes require perseverance in the face of inertia, resistance and frank disbelief.

It's important to realise that such attitudes cannot be driven into the organisation by force. Think again of the 'four-hour' target. Sure, the target is accepted and performance improves, but it is resented because it is not owned by the people who deliver it. The same is true of breakthrough attitudes.

Before you immediately (and rightly) complain that this 'breakthrough attitudes' idea is a load of woolly nonsense, let me admit that you have probably seen something similar before: 1980s-style 'thinking out of the box', anyone? Or how about a dot-com 'paradigm shift'? The concept of breakthrough attitudes sounds like many other pieces of consulting mumbo jumbo. And there are many companies or 'personal development forums' that rely on helping people 'overcome the impossible' or 'think the unthinkable'. On its own, I freely admit, 'breakthrough attitudes' seems largely empty. But it takes on real meaning when used in conjunction with *measured performance*.

This chapter therefore introduces you not just to a breakthrough attitude, but also to breakthrough results – the measurement of zero defects, or complaints, or accidents or whatever your target is. This requires rigour and numeracy. You don't achieve zero complaints by just telling people it's a good idea. You don't choose to go to the moon and then just cross your fingers. You invest time, effort and willpower – and in the case of moon landings, plenty of money – and then you measure every step of your progress. Measuring progress towards an 'unimaginable goal' is the key to achieving it.

The breakthrough result for your organisation may not be zero complaints – it may be something entirely different, more in keeping with your 'first or best' position. For example, my local hospital – the 'Hospital of Choice for Local People' – uses a 'promoter' score to measure how likely people are to recommend it to friends. Your organisation may propose being 'first or best' for something more clinical: zero HAIs (hospital-acquired infections) perhaps.

This chapter is not about the measurement itself – that is covered largely in the next chapter. This chapter is about what you must do in order to promote and create breakthrough attitudes.

THE IMPACT OF 'NEGATIVES'

This chapter focuses on attitude, so before we go further, we need to examine attitudes in more detail. In my implementation work, I have found it useful to divide staff of an organisation into three types, depending on their attitude.

A significant and important minority of your staff – let's say 10–20% – have a positive and uplifting attitude towards their work and towards exceptional patient care, which means they always try hard to look after their colleagues and patients with compassion and good humour. If anyone stays late, does an extra shift, or volunteers to help with a project, it will be one of these people. If anyone is complimented by a patient, it will probably be them. They offer suggestions for improving practice. They do research. They are creative, imaginative and good-humoured. These are the people that you want to work with, that you celebrate and thank good fortune for sending you. Without them, your organisation would probably falter. I call these your 'Positives'.

Working alongside this group is a much larger, more conservative group. For them, high performance is entirely optional – and it's an option they tend not to take. They do what is necessary to get by, performing their duties with reasonable care and diligence. On the whole, they work with good humour and without complaint. But they make sure they go home on time, and they don't usually volunteer or get involved in any extra work. They drift along, doing what's required. Probably 70–80% of your staff are like this. They are the lumpen middle. I call them your 'Neutrals'.

The remaining 5–10% per cent of staff are your problem children. This is a vocal group who think your organisation owes them a living irrespective of how they behave. Their level of competence varies: some may do their jobs effectively – many don't. Many of them spend much of their time being 'sick' (your inverted commas). They are self-obsessed and make poor team members. They are rarely promoted to anything as taxing as a leadership position. They spend their time complaining – and when not complaining, they seed vicious gossip that turns others against your organisation. They sap the energy of their colleagues, especially of their leaders and very often of their unions. They are, in short, poison. Your organisation would be better off without them. These are the 'Negatives'.

I've talked to hundreds of senior healthcare leaders. When I mention the idea of Negatives, all of them say much the same thing: 'I know exactly who you mean,' they sigh. 'There are only a few – but I can name every one of them.' It doesn't matter whether you're in the public sector, in private care or anywhere else for that matter. There are always just one or two of them that consume management time and effort, distracting leaders from the real task at hand and demotivating those around them.

The real problem is that Negatives are not just an annoyance. They can be dangerous – particularly if provoked. They also tend to hang out together and reinforce each other, and they breed discontent in others. It is your Negatives who hold back your organisation. When the patients complain about rude, unhelpful or inconsiderate behaviour, who, on the whole, is responsible for this? The Negatives. And what happens when you confront them? They go off sick, or claim harassment or unfair treatment. Some will even deliberately sabotage your organisation. What's worse is that this group have been at these tricks for years, often with multiple employers, and new leaders in particular don't realise what a challenge they are up against.

UNDERSTANDING THE CHALLENGE

Let's return to our idea of focus, and our ambition to create breakthrough attitudes that will generate breakthrough results. You can see that if we are going to develop breakthrough attitudes the Negatives will hold us back. It will be impossible to get to zero defects, zero complaints or any other breakthrough result with any Negatives in your organisation. By contrast, if your hospital were filled with Positives, delivering the very highest quality of patient care possible, then breakthrough results would be a cinch.

To conclude, if breakthrough attitudes means one thing, it means challenging and removing the effect of negative people in the organisation and promoting and celebrating the effort of our positive minority. It is only by doing so that we can transform our healthcare organisations. I will explain later in this chapter how this can be achieved.

WHAT IS A FOCUSED ORGANISATION?

A **focused** organisation DEMANDS breakthrough attitudes from its leaders and staff.
A **focused** organisation GENERATES breakthrough results.
A **focused** organisation PROMOTES positivity.
A **focused** organisation is INTOLERANT of negativity.

WHAT'S THE BENEFIT OF FOCUS?

As I said at the beginning of this chapter, it is at this point in the CAREFUL programme that transformation really begins. Breakthrough attitudes will, in time, deliver breakthrough results. These will provide a completely different level of clinical and quality outcomes, which will motivate staff to enjoy their daily work.

The benefit of focus is, in short, the total transformation of your organisation.

WHAT HAPPENS IF AN ORGANISATION LACKS FOCUS?

Organisations without focus are mediocre, because they are satisfied with mediocre performance. The same number of complaints as last year is good enough for them – no need to improve. And if mediocre patient care is good enough, then you can be sure that mediocre attempts at staff development will be just as prevalent.

Breakthrough attitudes, or lack of them, apply just as much to staff as to patients. Remember the hospital with the top 10 bland objectives in Chapter 5? In the same article on 'Trust Objectives' the hospital reminded us about the importance of people, as follows:

'The Trust's corporate objectives are on the intranet with links from the page to the full Annual Plan and to information about appraisals, personal development reviews and the knowledge and skills framework. Our target for the year is for 85% of all staff to have had an appraisal within the past 12 months.'

Great. For one in seven members of staff, their boss can't even find an hour a year to talk to them. And the trust board is so happy with this that they trumpet it as a success in the staff magazine. I'm totally motivated by that. How about you?

The trouble with mediocrity is that an organisation invariably tries to cover it up, or pretend that 'good enough' is 'fabulous'. This leads to a type of dishonesty that is detrimental to customers and staff alike. It also leads to cynicism among the people who are looking after our patients, because they realise they're working for an organisation that lacks integrity. We'll come back to this in Chapter 11.

WHY DON'T WE HAVE FOCUS IN OUR HEALTHCARE ORGANISATIONS?

I can suggest the following reasons:

1. **Lack of the right organisational qualities.** As I emphasised at the beginning of this chapter, without Commitment, Action, Responsiveness and Energy you don't stand much of a chance. Tackle them first.
2. **Lack of belief.** My experience of asking senior leaders whether they think it's possible for a hospital to achieve 'zero complaints' leads me to the conclusion that belief in excellence is a rare commodity.

3. **Fear of scale.** Even if the concept of breakthrough results is seen as possible, the size of the endeavour is enough to put off most people. They think it's better to keep their head down and deliver something smaller now.

4. **Short-termism.** There are few CEOs who are prepared to battle with their shareholders or the Department of Health to pursue long-term cultural change as a policy. Most are judged on the operational results delivered this quarter or next. Board members need to be motivated by long-term gain if they are to set up the organisation for success several years into the future.

5. **Negatives.** I covered this in detail above. With Negatives around, you'll never get anywhere near the breakthrough attitudes that you need – not just because of their attitude but because of the disproportionate drain on leaders' time that they cause and the insidious effect they have on Neutrals.

HOW CAN WE CREATE FOCUS IN OUR HEALTHCARE ORGANISATIONS?

If you do only one thing to create focus in your organisation, you must address negative attitudes.

Given my emphasis on the idea of Positives, Neutrals and Negatives, you will not be surprised to hear that the essential action you must take to make your organisation more focused involves working with these three groups. You need to do three things – and in this order:

- recognise and promote the behaviour and attitudes of Positives;
- encourage Neutrals to adopt more positive attitudes and behaviour; and
- change or remove the Negatives.

I can't stress enough how important this is to our overall goal of performance ownership. Removing the effect of negative attitudes is an absolute prerequisite. To undertake this you will need first to do some preparation. Here is my five-point plan.

1. Decide what positive/neutral/negative behaviour looks like

You need to work out who your Positives, Neutrals and Negatives are. You must do this without fuelling the grudge that exists in every Negative or undermining the good of the Positives. The exercise needs to be done with compassion and care and as objectively as possible. That means that preparation for this needs to be done with the full backing and understanding of the board, the senior leadership team, the unions, and the HR and legal departments. Yes, the legal department. If I know anything about Negatives, they'll be on to their lawyers before you can say 'performance review'. So stay awake. And please, bring in the unions early in this debate. Properly enrolled, they will be happy to help. Negatives make their lives hell too.

I advise all my clients to draw up a list of demonstrable and preferably measurable behaviours that you want to see in your organisation such as timeliness, level of absenteeism, number of compliments or complaints, time spent on improvement projects including audit, number of verbal or written warnings and so forth. Go back to the behavioural guidelines produced in Chapter 7, which your staff (probably your positives) drew up. Use all these to create a simple marking system which demonstrates who is positive, neutral or negative. I can't dictate what this looks like because it needs to fit with your organisation's idea of what it values in its people.

2. Train your leaders in how to address performance

I have trained hundreds of leaders, most of them 'first-level leaders'. They tell me that the most troubling thing they have to do is challenge poor performance, such as persistent lateness, rudeness and petty rule-breaking. Let me translate: the most difficult thing you will ever need to do as a leader is deal with Negatives.

Before going any further, you must provide training and support for leaders to have what we call the 'three conversations', which are described in more detail below. This must include training for senior leaders in how to support junior colleagues in these conversations. The HR department will already have a course that explains how to 'review' performance formally. The 'three conversations' are different, though, because they can happen at any time, which means on the 'shop floor' as well as in a more formal setting.

You must also teach leaders how to use the list that you have drawn up to identify Positives, Neutrals and Negatives in their ambit. Those that score above a certain limit are Positives, those that score below are likely to be Negatives and those in between... you get the picture. Importantly, this is merely a guide for leaders to make their own decisions about which members of staff are performing well or badly.

3. Identify and recognise the Positives

Using the list of demonstrable behaviours that you have drawn up, create a list of the Positives. Now ensure – you guessed it, by having a system and measuring it – that every positive member of staff has received positive feedback from their immediate line manager at least THREE times. Back this up with one or two from a more senior source. Don't worry. This is legal. No one will take you to a tribunal for telling them they're great.

The reason for the 'three times' is that psychological research shows that you need at least a three-to-one ratio of positive encounters to believe that you have a positive overall relationship with anyone.

4. Encourage and support the Neutrals

Once we have identified and recognised the Positives, we need to ensure that our leaders encourage the Neutrals to be more positive. They must encourage Neutrals to accept new challenges and must then provide the support that will make the Neutrals into high performers (remember our challenge/support model from Chapter 4). This will quickly improve the way that leaders are perceived.

THE DEAD WOOD

A ward leader who had been with the hospital for more than 20 years was frequently absent without reason. When at work, she was surly and uncooperative with staff and patients. The ward had high levels of staff turnover and consistently received low patient satisfaction scores. Clinical care was seen as poor and medical staff were reluctant to have patients on this ward. It took several months of coaching, followed by a difficult period of disciplinary procedures, before the hospital eventually removed her from the organisation. The effect on the ward was dramatic: improved patient satisfaction, better clinical outcomes and lower staff turnover. Despite the conflict, she remains on good terms with her colleagues. When she visited the hospital recently she confided she was much happier; being forced to change jobs had given her fresh direction.

THE THREE CONVERSATIONS

This is just an outline of the three conversations that your leaders all need to be confident of having with staff, both formally and informally.

Giving great feedback: reinforcing the Positives

Select a specific occasion or event. Ask them their opinion: how did it go for them? Give them your opinion: what you thought went well. Remind them of the positive impact they had on other people. Remind them that the organisation couldn't provide the great care that it does without such things. Then thank them. Sounds easy? Perhaps, but we're not used to doing it. It takes a bit of practice not to sound insincere, even though you mean it.

Pointing the way: encouraging the Neutrals

Ask them their opinion: how did it go for them? Give them your opinion: what you thought went well, what you thought could have been improved (they usually know – which is why you ask them first). Identify ways in which they could ensure it goes better next time. Remind them of the positive behaviour that they should reinforce. Remind them what a positive impact that would have. Remind them that the organisation needs people like them to provide great care. Thank them for their contribution. Sounds straightforward? Maybe – but the difficulty is making it positive and encouraging rather than emphasising the negatives. Also, we tend to talk too much, rather than listen to the other person's point of view.

Conversations without coffee: dealing with the Negatives

Ensure you have someone with you. Sit down in a place you can't be overheard. Take notes. Ask them what happened. Listen carefully to their view. Acknowledge their view. Assert the importance of the relevant standards or behaviours. Remind them that this is about caring for staff and patients. If necessary, go round the loop again: listen, acknowledge, assert.

At the end, explain that what they did is unacceptable and will not be tolerated. Explain that you will be making a note on file of this conversation. Sounds hard? Too right. But it's easier than you might think if you've been trained and are prepared and, most importantly, know you will be backed up by the organisation for having done this. And once you've done it a few times, it gets much easier.

5. Eliminate the Negatives

This used to be the hard part. Now it's not so hard. Your leaders will have generated enough goodwill from the majority of those they lead. The small group of Negatives are now easily identified because they will have received very little in the way of positive feedback. Negatives must be given every chance to improve, but, crucially, they must be challenged about their behaviour as soon as it occurs – not the next day, not next week, not at their yearly appraisal. Instead, whenever any of them acts in a negative way, the leader must identify the behaviour and eliminate it right away, every time. I suggest you check with your HR department to make sure every leader knows the procedure and is properly trained in having challenging conversations (see opposite page). The leader should ensure there is a witness to the conversation, that they take notes and that they file these with HR. It doesn't matter how trivial the offence, the leader must sit down and make it clear what is unacceptable, and make a note in the HR file. Every time. No excuses.

Eventually one of three things will happen to each of these negative people. They will either:

1. learn to behave as the organisation (and your patients and staff) want them to;
2. find this far too difficult and look for another job; or
3. sue you.

You'd better be ready for the last outcome because the real hard cases have been through this before – they've sliced through other organisations like a knife through butter. And because people aren't focused on eliminating negative behaviour, file notes tend to be absent, even for your worst employees. This makes dealing with negativity almost impossible. I'm no HR expert, but I do know that when things get nasty – and they will with a few people – you'll need all the evidence you can muster.

One last thing. Don't you dare give them a good reference when they leave. They'll only wreak havoc somewhere else.

SUPPORTING FOCUS – WHAT ELSE YOU WILL NEED TO DO

As well as removing the effect of Negatives on our organisation, there are three other areas that I would like to touch on that will support our efforts.

TRANSFORMING RECRUITMENT

To have a great organisation we must attract and retain the best staff – and develop the people we have. I've already talked about how we can create an environment where people want to stay and where we develop them fully. Here are some suggestions on how to ensure we recruit the right people in the first place – and get the best out of them when they arrive.

First, you should transfer assessment of new recruits and decisions about who gets hired to the team who will be working with them. This means setting up peer interviews, preferably using your high-performing individuals and abiding by their decisions. It also means giving recruits some work experience in the organisation before being employed. This need only be for a shift on a ward or for a period in the office. It's easy to impress a future boss during an interview – much less so future peers for an entire day. For existing staff, peer interviews can ensure there is no surprise when a new face appears. Both work experience and peer interviews put assessment in the hands of those best placed to judge. Leaders and the HR department appreciate giving some of the responsibility for recruitment to the staff who might otherwise disagree with their decisions. Also, new staff get a chance to really assess the culture of your organisation, making it easier for them to make the right decision.

Second, you must give recruits a real chance to make a positive impact on their new organisation to help them through what is often a difficult period. This means asking them for ideas about how things might be improved and asking for their critiques – both positive and negative – of the organisation. We recommend structured interviews with recent recruits after three weeks and then again after three months. People who have just joined can tell you how things are done elsewhere. They also have an outsider's view, which means they can see more clearly what's wrong with an organisation. They are a valuable source of new ideas, and that needs to be used to your advantage.

Three-week and three-month follow-up interviews make new staff feel valued. They also help the organisation benefit from best practices outside the organisation. The interviews are designed to protect new employees against the 'not invented here' attitude that we so often come up against in new organisations, where the new ideas that new employees bring in are automatically rejected. As ever, I recommend setting up proper systems to ensure that all new recruits are interviewed in this way and that their suggestions are carefully assessed.

TAKING INDUCTION SERIOUSLY

Most of us have been through an induction process in the first week of a new job, but too often this is about being shown the coffee machine and the fire escapes and then taken briefly through our tasks – in other words, policy and procedures rather than values and vision. This is a wasted opportunity. Induction should be a thorough and inspiring introduction to the organisation, what it stands for, and what the new recruit is expected to contribute. New employees need to be told about the first or best position and should be given a thorough introduction to behavioural guidelines and the hospital's processes. (See Chapter 10 for more about the value of process.) They should be inspired from the start that their new workplace is an organisation that is worth working for. Investing this kind of time and effort in people early on really pays off. In short, it is a chance to sow the seeds of performance ownership.

BREAKTHROUGH LEADERSHIP TRAINING

I have one final thought about breakthrough attitudes, which is that it's hard to leave the comfort of what you think is possible. I've worked with many leaders who are happy to 'manage' – they muddle along, putting in the same performance year after year. Shifting people into a whole separate gear is a difficult and sometimes frightening business. One of my favourite games is to get a group of people together and give them a dozen four-inch wood nails (the ones with the triangular head), one of which has been hammered into a block of wood. The challenge – and there are no tricks here – is to balance the remaining eleven nails on the one sticking out of the block. It's possible – but watching people react to this is an amazing study in the psychology of change.

Some people need more help accepting that the impossible is possible. I recommend providing support where it's needed.

CHAPTER 10

Uniform

'Get it right'

T his chapter is devoted to the subject of process, because I believe that results – which include cost savings and efficiencies – can improve significantly only if you improve your processes. So far in this book, I have talked exclusively about people and how to help them improve their performance, because it is the way in which people work together that makes it possible to achieve and sustain process improvements. That is why I always put people before process. But the time has come to tackle the thorny subject of process itself.

THE MAGIC OF PROCESS

The importance of process can hardly be overstated; day-to-day processes have to work pretty much flawlessly if your organisation is to be efficient, effective and financially healthy. In recent years, UK hospitals have spent a lot of time and millions of pounds pursuing the ideal of rigorous process improvement under the guise of Lean Thinking and its cousin, Six Sigma. These take principles and ideas culled from successful manufacturing firms such as Toyota, GM and Motorola and apply them to a healthcare setting. But as far as I can tell, none of them has underpinned this investment in process with a similar investment in people, such as I have been advocating in this book. I believe that by doing so, we can make process improvement truly sustainable.

Let me start with a simple definition: **processes define and control the way that people perform repetitive tasks.** That is the ideal, and that is what we should aim for. Processes should be both effective (people do the right thing) and efficient (they do it with as few resources and as quickly as possible). If processes are both of these things, it means that repetitive tasks are done right, on time, every time.

This may sound as if we want to turn all our highly trained staff into automatons. In fact, good process control has exactly the opposite result, allowing staff to offer 'service on top' – to care properly for their patients as individuals in an environment where things work as they should – as we shall discuss later in this chapter.

This chapter provides a rough guide to working with processes. Specifically, I am providing some very simple tools and ideas to help you and your staff improve their processes. This may seem to be the least exciting part of the CAREFUL programme – but it is where we deliver the efficiencies and cost savings that are so important.

THE PROBLEM WITH JOHN AND HIS BACKLOG

I mentioned John in Chapter 8. He was the accounting departmental leader for a multinational oil firm in a developing country. A period of growth and a merger had left him with a multitude of accounting systems, some confused staff and – most seriously – an enormous backlog of unpaid invoices. When I met him, his best estimate of the average time that it took for an invoice to be paid was over 90 days. Let's be clear. This was not policy. It was the reverse of what the company wanted. It was politically embarrassing for one of the world's largest companies to be effectively borrowing money from small, third-world businesses to finance its operations. This company was the biggest in the country and it was unintentionally putting some of its suppliers out of business. The accounting department itself was also daunted by the scale of the problem. It got in the way of their other duties and it caused friction and difficulties with the rest of the organisation. The accountancy team was despondent and unhappy.

It didn't take long to realise that there was a fundamental problem: every invoice was processed in a different way. Suppliers didn't know how to get paid, so some gave their invoices to the person who had supervised their work, some sent them to head office, some to the local operations plant. The invoices went by a myriad of different routes before they arrived at the accounting department. And then the fun started. Different parts of the team processed the invoices in different ways, depending on what they had previously been taught. Not surprisingly, it was a mess. What was worse, it was clear that simply driving down the backlog using overtime wasn't going to prevent another one from developing the next month. In fact, the department had employed several more full-time staff and the problem had got worse, not better. So my company was hired to sort out the problem.

The first job was to help the suppliers understand how to get paid. John agreed with all the suppliers how and where to present all future invoices. This took a while, because there were thousands of suppliers and changing their habits was not easy. Together, the department agreed on what should happen to the invoices when they arrived in the department. John took the opportunity to create new sub-teams, which dealt with different sizes of invoice (and therefore took care to process 'small business' invoices more quickly – the opposite of what had been happening before).

After a year of effort, using an Action Team run by one of his deputies, John reported that the average time it took to process an invoice had fallen – and he knew exactly what it was, because part of the plan was to measure results. The last time we spoke, it was down from 90 to 28 days and was still falling.

I use this story of a relatively simple, non-clinical situation because it highlights some important principles about process:

1. Processes exist only inside the heads of those involved. People tend to follow their own idea of the process, rather than what's in the instruction manual. This has two implications – if a process is to be followed, first it must be **simple enough to remember**; and second, you have to **teach correctly to everyone the part of the process in which they are involved**. The invoices in our story were sent to pretty much anyone in the entire business because the suppliers didn't understand their role. The same thing applied to the invoice processing department. To make the process work, all the suppliers and all the staff needed to learn that invoices had to go to Point A for payment and absolutely nowhere else. *Making processes so simple and obvious that everyone remembers their own role correctly is the key.* Only then does everybody do the right thing. This is critical to improving processes. Having a complicated process is worse than useless, unless you can find a way to get people to follow it, which is hard. If people don't remember their part of the process, they will simply make it up as they go along, and will get it wrong. Bundles of invoices end up in the wrong place. By analogy, our patients may go missing or be wrongly treated.

2. Processes need to be measured if they are to be improved. In my example of John and his invoices, we established the average time to payment as the key measure we were going to use. Everything else was subsidiary to this number – even the daunting backlog. I've said this before, but will repeat it here:

numbers give people a way to concentrate on what is important and to solve problems. Numbers provide a measure of success, which can be celebrated.

3. All your processes matter, not just the clinical ones. Simple processes, such as that of paying invoices, can affect your organisation's financial performance and your reputation just as much as the sexy clinical pathways. It's no good bringing someone to endoscopy if you've failed to pay your suppliers and there's no equipment. I met a doctor who invoiced a London hospital for some work and it took them more than three months to pay him. In effect, he was financing the NHS – which seemed unfair. So he switched to using a locum agency and the hospital now pays 30% more for his time. There is a huge amount of unnecessary cost in healthcare that is hidden in this way.

4. The problem is always beyond where you can see. If one person could see the whole of any process then problems would soon be resolved. Unfortunately, all processes cross boundaries inside and outside your organisation, so most people see only one part of the process. The bigger the organisation, the more true this is. The solution is to simplify and clarify the process, as we'll discuss in the section on Process Block Diagrams (page 110). This is also one of the reasons for using cross-functional Action Teams, as described in Chapter 6.

5. Real improvement takes time. Hitting John's backlog with a huge overtime effort would have solved the problem in just a few weeks. Changing processes, solving problems, incrementally improving things – these take time and real collaboration. Which is why, again, you have to put people before processes.

WHAT IS A UNIFORM ORGANISATION?

A **uniform** organisation PERFORMS its repetitive tasks correctly – first time, every time.

A **uniform** organisation continually MEASURES and IMPROVES its processes to generate better results.

A **uniform** organisation STANDARDISES its processes where possible.

A **uniform** organisation DESCRIBES and COMMUNICATES its processes clearly.

WHAT'S THE BENEFIT OF UNIFORMITY?

The benefits of UNIFORMITY are threefold. The first is obvious. By creating a culture of continuous process-led improvement, results will improve. Properly pursued, process improvement creates enormous efficiencies and saves money.

Secondly, performance ownership begins to develop as staff see the connection between their actions and the published performance figures. This improves motivation and staff retention and improves the human capital value of the organisation, as described in Chapter 2.

The final benefit is more subtle – and initially counterintuitive. Uniformity actually allows more flexibility in the way that patients are treated and the way in which non-process aspects of care are delivered. Paradoxically, standardisation allows for more individualisation.

Let me explain.

I am privileged to have an educational supervisor who is not only enthusiastic and supportive but is also a formidable diagnostician. We were talking about processes the other day. 'Everybody's illness is as individual as their thumbprint,' he said. 'And you can put that in your book.' And I have – because the point he makes is an important one. The unending variability between patients and between episodes of illness for each patient, added to the incompleteness of our knowledge about the individuals and their conditions, makes true 'standardisation' across all patients not only undesirable but impossible. They are all different and they all need to treated as individuals.

However, pursuing uniformity where it is possible delivers huge efficiency gains. It allows the carers some time and headspace to give the right level of individual attention to patients – the 'service on top' that I mentioned earlier. It's clear that if we spend our time as clinicians on the phone or on the computer chasing inefficient processes, we get stressed amongst the muddle. Sadly, as a clinician I spend much of my time on the shop floor doing just that: chasing up blood results, calling other doctors to ask them to see the patient and so on. Yet it needn't always be so. Just recently one of my hospitals introduced a system of automatically calling porters. Prior to that, every time we wanted to move a patient, we had to bleep the porter, wait by the phone for their return call, explain what we needed, put a written request in a box...

and so it goes on. Now, we just type a request into a computer and (by magic, it sometimes seems) a porter appears and takes the patient to where they need to go. This probably frees up at least 20 or 30 minutes of my working day. With this time, I can more easily talk to patients and their relatives and give more thought to their problems, which is what I should be doing.

Looking back at John and his invoice processors, I remember that when I first met them, they were unable to answer queries on the phone because they were so busy being inefficient. By the time the process was sorted, they had a dedicated help-line for suppliers, which was manned for 12 hours a day. This responsiveness was possible only because of their new, efficient processes.

WHAT HAPPENS IF AN ORGANISATION LACKS UNIFORMITY?
The main consequences are
- frustration
- inefficiency
- damaged reputation
- wasted time
- lost opportunities
- work that has to be redone
- poor levels of service
- unhappy patients
- demoralised staff

It is these problems that have prompted such an enormous effort in recent years to improve processes using the Lean and Six Sigma techniques that are so prevalent. As I've said, this effort is well directed but under-supported, as there is not enough investment in people-related improvements.

WHY DON'T WE HAVE UNIFORMITY IN OUR HEALTHCARE ORGANISATIONS?
There are three main reasons why uniformity is hard to achieve.

1. Lack of process management ability. No one teaches process management at school, certainly not at nursing or medical college. It is also accompanied by a lot of jargon, which makes it sound difficult. I've tried to simplify this admittedly huge subject into a few simple tools, but even these will need to be taught to all leaders and staff before they can be used effectively.

2. Lack of supporting culture and behaviour. I've emphasised throughout this book the need to put people before process. Creating uniform processes and developing a culture of performance ownership requires a huge amount of discretionary effort and goodwill on the part of staff. Most organisations lack the qualities that I've discussed of commitment, action, responsiveness and energy, which are the necessary foundations for this sort of work.

3. The vicious circle of inefficiency. There is nothing quite like inefficient processes to burn time, resources and goodwill. Rising above the quagmire in truly inefficient organisations is hugely difficult for this reason. There is an expression: if you're too busy running in circles to buy a map, you'll never get anywhere. Or, perhaps more accurately, it's hard to remember that your job is to drain the swamp when you're up to your arse in alligators.

FOUR THINGS YOU NEED TO KNOW ABOUT PROCESS

Out of everything that I know about process, there are four things I would like to present, which should help you to understand, manage and improve the processes in your organisation. They are:

- a definition of process
- Process Block Diagrams
- the principle of DCI and the DADA model
- Performance Boards

WHAT IS A PROCESS (OR, HOW DO YOU MAKE A MUG OF TEA)?

I spend much of my time talking about processes – too much, some might say – but as a result, I have come up with a couple of simple definitions of a process. The first definition is:

- *A series of tasks which, taken sequentially, accomplish a task.*

In this slightly clunky definition, all processes are made up of tasks, which can themselves be split into a number of further tasks. So any process can be part of another process. As a trivial example, we can split making a mug of

PROCESS VS THE REST OF THE WORLD

The word 'process' sits in a pantheon of other similar ideas. Here's a small selection of terms that may seem the same as 'process':

- Audit
- Patient Pathways
- Guidelines
- Policies and Procedures
- Standards

All of these things above are necessary, but they are not the same as process. In my view, what distinguishes process from these other terms is that 'process' implies the measurement of outputs and an emphasis on performance and continuous, as opposed to intermittent, improvement.

tea into three tasks: boil water, put teabag in mug and prepare. Then we can split the first of these tasks further into: grab kettle, fill with water, switch on and wait… and so on (see diagram overleaf). Making a mug of tea can, if we wish, be made infinitely detailed.

Another, more practical definition of a process is:

- *A series of actions that converts a group of inputs into an output.*

Riveting, I know, but stick with me. We take cold water and a kettle (inputs) and get boiling water (output). We then take mug, teabag and milk (inputs), mix them with the boiling water (input) and we get a mug of tea (output).

Exactly how you decide to split the processes in your organisation into sub-processes is arbitrary, but a good way to decide how to split them is to identify what are your most useful inputs/outputs. It is the outputs that are then used to measure the efficiency or effectiveness of your process.

In the case of our mug of tea, it could be number of mugs of tea produced or volume of boiling water. Outputs can also be tested for quality (the final temperature of the tea before serving, for instance).

Having defined our measurable outputs, we can then make a person or department responsible for delivering outputs of a certain quality, which in turn gives us the measurable results that we need for improvement.

GETTING A HANDLE ON THINGS: PROCESS BLOCK DIAGRAMS

I have worked in a great many hospitals in my time. They all do things differently. In just my speciality of Emergency Medicine, the differences between hospitals are enormous: local policies, layout of the department, availability of local services, even the type of telephone system. I have never been to any department where this is written down in any sort of order for every new starter.

Bearing in mind the most important principle of this chapter – which is that processes are only of any use when they can be easily remembered and followed – we need a mechanism for achieving this that is reliable and quick. I've seen things such as process diagram maps and ISO9000 documents which are dense, impenetrable and impossible to read or carry. These documents have their purposes, I'm sure, but communication is not high on the list.

I've rarely seen a document that is actually designed to help staff learn how a process works. The fact is that staff tend to learn their processes from their peers. They get 'shown around' on the first day and 'pick it up as they go along'. Much of what you have to learn as a new starter is about policy and local guidelines rather than process, as we discussed in Chapter 9. But process is important to performance, so it's a mistake to overlook it.

To overcome this problem, I have developed a simple way to describe a process – the Process Block Diagram. Its three principal features are:

1. a series of sub-processes across the top;
2. a series of 'tasks' hanging off those sub-processes; and
3. a series of outputs at the end of each sub-process.

As an example, the Process Block Diagram for making our mug of tea is shown opposite.

Importantly, the entire diagram MUST fit on to one page – it is, after all, an aide-memoire, and will be ineffective if too long. I advise clients to create these for their organisation and give them to all members of staff, so that everyone is aligned in their tasks and everyone understands where they fit into the overall scheme of things.

As a comparison, the diagram on page 113, which was created by a client of mine, shows a real-life situation in a hospital. It summarises the overriding process for the entire enterprise – from the patient's perspective. The boxes are shaded differently for each department.

The simplicity of this diagram avoids the need for complex decision boxes and spaghetti-like diagrams. Those may work for computer code and manufacturing cars, but for service industries these block diagrams are much better. Obviously not EVERY patient goes through EVERY box – just like tea might have milk, sugar, both or neither – but it describes all the things that any patient could go through, so all eventualities are covered. Clearly, where necessary, each one of the little boxes is backed up by another process diagram, which describes in detail what happens in each department.

I have found these diagrams to be useful at many different levels – from the whole organisation right down to individual areas. They serve to clarify, communicate and simplify, rather than clutter or confuse. And, at the risk of repeating myself too often: that's the point.

PROCESS IMPROVEMENT: THE MODELS OF DCI AND DADA

There are two models that I use when I talk about processes to help people think about how to improve them.

The first of these is straightforward. DCI stands for:

• Describe: we've already done this with our simple block diagrams.

- Control: ensure we measure and monitor the outputs regularly enough.
- Improve: find ways to change the process in order to improve.

Simple enough. But how often is it consciously done? DCI helps to remind us that merely writing a process down is only the first step – processes also need to be measured and changed in order to improve performance.

The second acronym, DADA, stands for:
- Data: make sure you collect the data you need to improve things.
- Analysis: spend time working out what the data is telling you.
- Decision: agree as a team what needs to change in order to improve.
- Action: go out and change the process.

This is normally written as a loop like this:

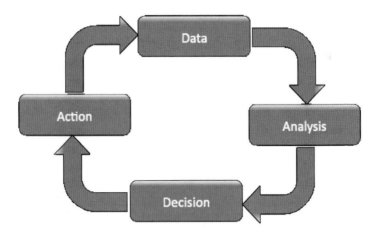

This loop reminds us that improving processes is a continuous habit, which requires constant monitoring. Improvement comes about by consciously trying to change how the processes work, in order to deliver better results.

The analysis and decisions are taken within a meeting environment – often weekly or monthly team meetings. This is why I stressed meeting continence so strongly in the earlier chapter on action. Meeting skills are of critical importance when improving processes.

Hospital Process Summary

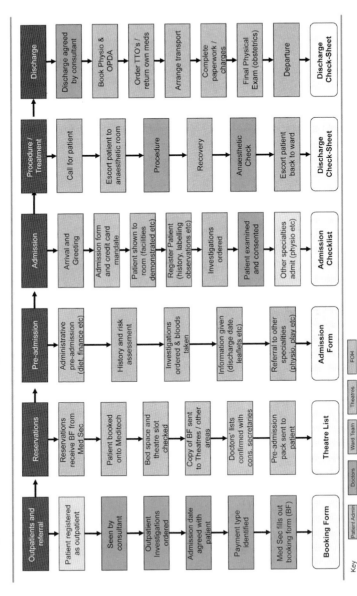

Outpatients and referral
- Patient registered as outpatient
- Seen by consultant
- Outpatient Investigations ordered
- Admission date agreed with patient
- Payment type Identified
- Med Sec fills out booking form (BF)
- **Booking Form**

Reservations
- Reservations receive BF from Med Sec
- Patient booked onto Meditech
- Bed space and theatre slot checked
- Copy of BF sent to Theatres / other areas
- Doctors' lists confirmed with cons. secretaries
- Pre-admission pack sent to patient
- **Theatre List**

Pre-admission
- Administrative pre-admission (diet, finance etc)
- History and risk assessment
- Investigations ordered & bloods taken
- Information given (discharge date, leaflets etc)
- Referral to other specialties (physio, play etc)
- **Admission Form**

Admission
- Arrival and Greeting
- Admission form and credit card mandate
- Patient shown to room (facilities demonstrated etc)
- Register Patient (history, labelling, observations etc)
- Investigations ordered
- Patient examined and consented
- Other specialties admit (physio etc)
- **Admission Checklist**

Procedure / Treatment
- Call for patient
- Escort patient to anaesthetic room
- Procedure
- Recovery
- Anaesthetic Check
- Escort patient back to ward
- **Discharge Check-Sheet**

Discharge
- Discharge agreed by consultant
- Book Physio & OPDA
- Order TTO's / return own meds
- Arrange transport
- Complete paperwork / changes
- Final Physical Exam (obstetrics)
- Departure
- **Discharge Check-Sheet**

Key: Patient Admin | Doctors | Ward Team | Theatres | FOH

113

NOT UNDER THE BUSHEL: PERFORMANCE BOARDS

One last idea is worth exploring before we finish this discussion of processes. Given that well-run processes are used to improve the performance of the organisation, it's important to publicise the good work that is done, for the sake of both patients and staff.

In one hospital in which I work, every member of the department is sent a daily update of the performance against the four-hour target. This is great, but a daily snapshot gives no idea about trends and is not a subject of much discussion. The email lands in the inbox, I usually pause to admire the fact that it's green – rather than red or amber – and then I discard it.

How much better it would be to have a Performance Board – a small section of the department's wall dedicated to informing us how well staff are doing on their targets, not just today, but this week and this month. I strongly advise all my clients to use graphs to show results rather than just numbers. They are easier to read and faster to interpret by anyone who is passing. Performance Boards must reflect the commitments that the organisation has made and should therefore cover the Three Circles: people, patients and operations.

If we are going to promote performance ownership, then staff must know what their performance is – good or bad. Performance Boards are an easy way to do this.

HOW CAN WE CREATE UNIFORMITY IN OUR HEALTHCARE ORGANISATIONS?

If you do only one thing to create uniformity, implement Performance Boards throughout each department – and back this up by teaching process management.

The reason for this is that by implementing Performance Boards, staff will learn to value, and eventually own, their performance.

I always advise my clients to start small and not bite off too much at once. Make sure each department – having been properly trained in the subject of process management – develops a simple process block diagram for their area and then measures initially just ONE output. If you remember John's overstretched invoice processors, we encouraged them to focus on the average time to process invoices. When staff have learned to do this, it's a relatively easy step to move on to more complex and more numerous targets and measures, and more detailed process designs.

Process improvement should be a topic that is regularly discussed in the leadership academies that I wrote about in Chapter 8. I include it in all leadership programmes that I run.

SUPPORTING UNIFORMITY – MAPPING AND RATIONALISING THE ORGANISATIONAL MANAGEMENT SYSTEM

As I suggested earlier, process management is a huge and complex subject. I have only really touched on what I think are the essentials that every leader needs to know. To back up the work that each department needs to do, there must be overall responsibility for managing the processes that interlink across departments.

For instance, getting A&E performance right – admitting and treating patients within four hours – requires that the Emergency Department understand and manage their processes effectively. That in itself is no good if patients reach a bottleneck further down the line or if the radiology, pathology or outpatients departments are unable to fulfil their requirements. These departments rely on understanding what the others are doing and making sure that changes taking place in one area are properly understood and taken into account elsewhere. Anyone who has worked in a large organisation will recognise this problem: 'They can't do that!' you think, or 'Since when has that changed? No one told me!' It's common.

To solve such hospital-wide systemic problems requires that overall leadership and management of the hospital is handled as a whole. For this, a well-run management system needs to be designed. I call this overall management system view the 'decision-making and reporting system' or DMRS. This may be a slightly clunky description, but it helps to give it a name. In order to run at all, every hospital has to have a DMRS. The trouble is, not all of the people responsible for running it know how to describe it or – most importantly – how it works.

At the risk of simplifying this too far, let me define a DMRS as the totality of meetings, documents and other systems – both manual and computerised – that allow staff to take decisions. Without doubt, that's a lot of management stuff, and to map and understand how it all works can seem daunting, if not impossible. I use a mapping system – which can easily take up an entire wall – that places these elements on a large grid of frequency vs function. In other words, down one side is an axis of yearly/monthly/weekly/daily and along the top are elements that will be recognisable from the Three Circles model. Most simply, we would look at 'operations, patients and staff'. In a more detailed analysis we might include 'quality' or 'safety' or even 'infection'.

We then show how information and decision-making flows take place between decision-making forums. These links highlight where information is missing, or where duplications take place. We can then understand more easily how decisions taken in different places affect or feed into other parts of the organisation. Eventually, we can design and change this DMRS to make it more transparent and more efficient.

Mapping and changing the DMRS can be a time-consuming and difficult business, but when completed, just like Process Block Diagrams, it helps people to understand how the hospital works and so can deliver enormous benefits. It helps senior leaders, in particular, rationalise the enormous number of meetings and decision-making forums that exist in a complex organisation, and it can make information flow more easily.

CHAPTER 11

Leading

'*Be proud*'

I was talking to the CEO of a small independent healthcare facility one day, trying to explain the concept of performance ownership and how important it could be to the patient's experience.

'Who do you bank with?' I asked.

'First Direct,' she replied.

'*That's* what I'm talking about.'

'Ah. I get it,' she said. Then she paused and smiled slightly wistfully. 'They're just so great, aren't they?'

I nodded. 'Yes. They are.'

For a couple of moments, we were both lost in a sort of reverie – as if we had discovered we were both fans of an obscure 1970s rock band and were remembering the tracks we'd listened to as teenagers. In fact, we were both thinking the same thing. How great, we were agreeing, is our bank.

Our *bank*?

Yes, that's right. So, for the record, I'll say it now. If you, my reader, are not banking with First Direct, then you're with the wrong bank. If you think that all banks are the same and that you are stuck with irritating, uncaring and useless bureaucratic machines, then think again. Do yourself a favour: move your personal banking to First Direct. I guarantee you won't regret it.

I am doing something here called customer advocacy. This is the holy grail for all brand managers. I am advising you that you should leave your current bank and move to First Direct. I get nothing in return for this advocacy. I love my bank enough that I'm willing to drum up more business for them in public.

Good God, you must think. How sad is that? What could prompt such behaviour? What could First Direct have done to deserve this? The simple answer is that they have been utterly RESPONSIVE to everything that I've needed. From the first moment of contact, they are obviously COMMITTED to customer service. They don't say that they are – they just get on with it. From the customer's point of view their processes are completely UNIFORM – everything works right first time because everyone you speak to knows what they are doing. What's more, everyone you speak to has a real sense of ENERGY – they are actually enjoying what they do. They are, in short, the LEADING bank for customer service.

I once met a senior leader from HSBC (which owns First Direct) who was Operations Director for First Direct for many years. He told me that working there was the most enjoyable job he had ever had. He also told me that the bank focuses extraordinary amounts of effort on nurturing its call-centre staff. (According to one woman in the call centre that I spoke to, the company has been known to lay on fairground rides in the car park to compensate staff for working over a bank holiday weekend.) Its induction period lasts many weeks, and its employment contracts are extremely flexible. Its staff turnover is tiny.

It also makes good use of its customer loyalty – it uses real customers in its advertisements.

FULL CIRCLE

Having said all that, it must be noted that First Direct is not great in *every* way. From talking to other members of the banking industry, I find that First Direct is really just a bit player. In comparison with other high-street banks, and to the retail arm of its parent company, First Direct is tiny. A minnow. It doesn't turn in the greatest profit margin either. And its growth is nothing to write home about.

Nonetheless, First Direct is a leading organisation because it has reached its first or best position. It was the first non-branch bank (way back in 1987) and it is clearly the best in its commitment to customer service and customer loyalty. And that is what makes the difference to customers. First Direct is a first or best (in its case, both first and best) organisation. Both its staff and its customers know it, and revel in it.

Which brings us neatly back to the fifth chapter of this book, which discussed commitment. You will remember that I said that organisations need to create a first or best position and then pursue that.

The final stage of creating a CAREFUL organisation is to reinforce this position so that it comes alive for the people who work for it and who interact with it – our patients and our staff.

This return to the principles of the commitment stage helps the organisation continually to reinforce the behaviour that will underpin success.

TRUE LEADERS

The trouble with being truly leading – by which we mean first or best in your field – is that it's rare. Really rare. I have used First Direct as an example in this chapter. I also mentioned John Lewis in the introduction. And from my own experience outside healthcare, I would probably add Virgin Atlantic to that list. And that's just about it. Sorry to all those PR organisations that want to describe their organisations as 'leading' – I'm afraid my experience is that most are mediocre at best. Mostly they are deluded or simply mendacious.

Within healthcare, the list of organisations that have a 'first or best' position – backed up by a reputation with patients that makes them truly 'leading' – is notable for its brevity. Personally, I would put the Marsden (cancer), Maudsley (psychiatry) and Stoke Mandeville (spinal) on the list. After that it becomes difficult. I'm not saying there aren't any more; I just don't know of any. And I've been looking.

Just the other day, there was a possibility that I would need to seek out a hospital for an elective admission. A friend who works as a doctor in the area helped me to weigh up the advantages and disadvantages of several local hospitals, all of which I know quite well. Not one of them leaped out as the one I would prefer to be treated at. I have mixed reports from patients, friends and colleagues about all of them.

The fact is, that I have never worked in – or even heard of – a general, acute care hospital in this country which I could describe as 'leading'.

ARE YOU A LEADING ORGANISATION?

Before you get irritated by my claim, let me ask you to try a thought experiment. I'm assuming that you and your organisation are absolutely committed to great patient care, so I want you to imagine this.

If any two of your patients sat down in a room and discovered by chance that they had both been treated at your hospital, what would they say? Could you absolutely guarantee that they would wistfully stare into the distance and say: 'Oh, such a great place! I tell everyone that they should go there to be treated.'

The point is that I can guarantee that any two First Direct customers would do that. That's the difference.

WHAT IS A LEADING ORGANISATION?

A **leading** organisation is FIRST or BEST in its field.

A **leading** organisation demonstrates FIRST or BEST results.

A **leading** organisation reinforces its FIRST or BEST position with both customers and staff.

WHAT'S THE BENEFIT OF LEADING?

To understand the benefit of being a leading organisation, we should return to the Three Circles diagram (Chapter 2). You will notice that there is an arrow that runs from 'Reputation' to 'Motivation' and from 'Quality' to 'Motivation'. There is also an arrow that runs from 'Reputation' to 'Demand'.

What this means is that a leading organisation can derive maximum benefit from both the quality of its work and its reputation. It can improve motivation by reminding staff of these two things. It can also use its reputation – both directly with advertising and indirectly by creating 'customer advocates' – to create more demand from patients.

WHAT HAPPENS IF AN ORGANISATION IS NOT LEADING?

By failing to pursue a first or best position, organisations put themselves at risk of being bad-mouthed, not to mention distrusted, by their customers or patients. Organisations that accept second-best position (or worse) demotivate their staff and give patients or customers a reason to talk negatively of their experiences. Research suggests that a dissatisfied customer will tell 20 people about their experience, whereas a satisfied customer will tell four. A poor reputation will demotivate staff and scare off existing and potential customers. Demotivated staff then create a vicious circle of deteriorating services and more customers take flight. And so it goes on.

At its worst, organisations pretend to be leading. My favourite example of this is my mobile phone operator. As I wait on the line, often for ages, to speak to an uninterested, poorly trained and demotivated member of their call-centre staff, I am reminded by a recorded voice that 'We are committed to customer service'. This is self-evidently untrue. Such gratuitous posturing simply makes the poverty of its customer service more obvious, and provides a reason to distrust the organisation. Not surprisingly, I left that company some years ago – although I failed to find any leading mobile phone operator that compares with First Direct.

WHY DO WE HAVE SO FEW LEADING HEALTHCARE ORGANISATIONS?

We could blame unbalanced targets, lack of collaboration, unwillingness to listen to staff and customers, poor leadership, an inability to address negative attitudes, or broken processes. More sensibly, we could blame all of these things together.

The reason there are so few leading organisations is that it takes all the qualities of a CAREFUL organisation to get there.

I mentioned in Chapter 4 the implementation skills that are needed to transform your organisation. I've now covered in Chapters 5 to 11 all the qualities that an organisation must cultivate, using those skills.

For the most part, it takes time – often years – to turn an organisation around. Until leaders, shareholders and the Department of Health are willing to pursue this leading position, then we, as patients and relatives, will be treated by organisations that fall short of that ideal.

HOW TO BECOME A LEADING ORGANISATION

As I've suggested, the way to become a leading organisation is to put in place the building blocks of a CAREFUL organisation as described in the previous chapters.

The trick is to do this with honesty and integrity, rather than resorting to spin. Using the Performance Boards that we mentioned in the last chapter is key – it is here that you will find the true performance of your organisation.

However, the simplest and most important thing that you can do is to instigate a reward and recognition programme that truly reflects the behaviour and attitude that underpins your first or best position.

I worked with an organisation recently where they had 'Employee of the Quarter' posted at the front desk. At first I was impressed. Sadly, it turned out that no one really took this seriously. There was little leadership appetite for it and the candidates were proposed, somewhat reluctantly, by departmental leaders.

By contrast, BP has a series of 'Helios' awards delivered to teams across the organisation that have delivered something extraordinary. The awards are fiercely fought for. The awards are in the categories that are considered important to the values of the company (innovation, for instance) and they are awarded nationally by each president. Award-winners then run-off against each other regionally and globally. The winners get to fly to London to shake hands with the global CEO.

Your hospital may not be able to fly its high-performers across the globe, but it can put in place a system that recognises the discretionary effort of individuals and teams – and the CEO can spend time congratulating these people.

Such recognition systems are not difficult to implement, but they must underpin the values of the organisation and reinforce the first or best position. And they must be genuine.

CHAPTER 12

Transforming the NHS

It is not possible to write a book about performance ownership and the transformation of healthcare institutions without an attempt to set this in the wider context of the system in which it is delivered. It is with some trepidation that I am going to dip my toe into the roiling waters that surround the NHS and healthcare reform.

A few days ago, a young man in his twenties was brought in by ambulance because he couldn't sleep. He thought that he was going mad. Given that he'd drunk nearly a bottle of vodka and taken three 'legal high' tablets, as well as cocaine, ecstasy and diazepam, that was hardly surprising. He spent a few hours being assessed, examined and having blood tests. By the time we discharged him, he was feeling better. I had a similar experience early in my career, when an 18-year-old student arrived by ambulance. She had cut her finger on a baked bean tin and as her parents weren't home, she didn't know what to do – so she called 999. We put a plaster on it and sent her home.

It's worth comparing these stories to that of a woman in her seventies who I treated some months ago. She arrived one afternoon with back pain and sat in the waiting room, uncomplaining, for a couple of hours before I saw her. She'd been to see her GP with the same problem and he had given her paracetamol. She had continued to suffer badly until she was persuaded to attend A&E because she was now almost unable to walk due to the pain.

When I examined her, I found that she was in the advanced stages of undiagnosed cancer. She looked like a Belsen victim. Her back pain was caused by the extensive destruction and collapse of her vertebrae. She weighed less than 40kg. As we began the task of trying to ease her pain, she grabbed my arm and kissed my hand. 'You are so kind,' she said. 'So kind.' Her suffering upset me and that image has stayed with me for a long time.

When I mentioned this woman to one of my consultants, she said: 'Of course. A typical pre-NHS patient.'

These two stories graphically illustrate the dilemma of free healthcare. Without the NHS, the elderly woman – poor and friendless – would probably have died without any support. She certainly would not have been able to afford the treatment that she received towards the end of her life. In a developed society, no one need suffer in that way. Yet by providing free healthcare unquestioningly we encourage those who have never lived without this service to treat it, just like the first of these patients, with what seems like contempt.

And yet it isn't contempt. I have stressed from the start of this book the importance of numbers in managing our healthcare institutions. Whether measuring patient experience or the outputs of processes, it is the numbers that tell us how to act. It is a lack of numbers that is at the root of the behaviour of the two young people described above.

Patients and their families are unable to *value* the service they receive from the NHS because they have no way to *measure* that value.

I have laid out in this book a way in which healthcare leaders can attempt the difficult task of improving the hospitals and other institutions that, in the majority of cases, will be part of the NHS. There is no doubt, however, that the overall cost and efficiency of the NHS as well as the motivation of staff is undermined by the requirement to give unnecessary treatment to people who are basically well or who could look after themselves. As well as providing an essential service for a compassionate society, the NHS contributes to a creeping 'medicalisation' of normal life.

And yet quite clearly, the extreme opposite would be no more preferable. The provision of healthcare exclusively through private medical insurance leads to a situation in which my elderly lady would have no doubt died, in excruciating pain, at home, alone and uncared for.

However, this dilemma is partly solvable. By seeking a compromise between the two prevailing models – government-funded universal coverage, free at the point of delivery, and private provision delivered through personal insurance – we can find a 'third way' that maximises the benefits of each.

I am no health economist. I take my preferred model from the writing of Tim Hartford, 'Undercover Economist' at *The Financial Times*. In this model, all patients receive a government-funded allowance for discretionary medical spend, which they save throughout their life. A few thousand pounds per year, perhaps, which can be spent on anything: prescriptions, GP and A&E visits, elective surgery and even complementary therapies that are not normally covered by the NHS. This spending can be augmented by private contributions, or by using the allowances of friends and families.

But this is not all. This discretionary spend is complemented by free government provision for treatment for catastrophic or unavoidable illness: emergency surgery, hospitalisation for unexpected ill-health and the support of chronic conditions. In short, the government insures its population not against *everything*, but against those expensive eventualities which private insurance companies try to avoid. The government then provides enough allowance to give patients purchasing power where it is appropriate, which also gives them a real understanding of the cost – and value – of the care they receive. No one needs to choose which hospital they go to after a car crash, but they will always want to choose where to have their baby.

I have no doubt that such a system would have its problems. Regulation, standards, the care of children and vulnerable adults and assessing the 'dividing line' between discretionary and non-discretionary spend would all be cause for debate. There would also be issues of public health, and we would need to make sure that people did not receive inappropriate treatment – not all headaches need a CT scan. But it would be a debate based on the principle that no one should become so sick it makes them poor, and no one should be so poor that it makes them sick.

While healthcare would remain free at the point of delivery, this model would undermine the divisive question of 'private vs public' by giving real purchasing power to patients and their families: actual patient choice, rather than 'government-approved' choice. Money would *come with* – rather than in some unclear fashion 'follow' – the patient.

Most importantly, from the point of view of transforming healthcare in the way that I have outlined, this purchasing power would provide the motivation for individual institutions to make the changes that I have described in this book. These changes include being transparent and open about patient outcomes, improving the experience of care for patients and their families and creating a great place to work for staff, all of which are vital to improving healthcare.

During my medical career, I have been privileged to work with some of the most exceptional, capable, talented and compassionate people that I have ever met. I have mentioned just a few of these people in this book. In my view, we owe it to our patients to engage with this extraordinary pool of human capital and, by doing so, bring about a real transformation in healthcare.